IMPORTANT!
Instructions for Parents

- To use Summer Math Skills Sharpener, simply tear off a page and have your child complete it. The book is designed to be used *3-4 days per week for 10 weeks.*
- Our math books now support the Common Core Curriculum and the Standards of all 50 states. Therefore, some materials may not have been presented to your child. Please allow your child to skip concepts not yet learned. Introduce new concepts only if your child shows readiness.
- Check answers immediately for optimal feedback. An answer sheet and solution pages are provided at the back of the book. (**Solution pages represent only ONE method of solving each problem.**) A Lesson Tracker has been added for your convenience.
- "Help Pages" have been added at the front of the book to clarify certain concepts.
- Allow your child to use a calculator only for those problems marked "Calculator Skill."
- When solving division problems with remainders, students should use fractions or decimals rounded off to the nearest hundredth.
- When solving fraction problems, students should reduce answers to the lowest possible terms.
- Pages entitled "Brain Aerobics" are located at the back of the book. Have your child complete one page per week for extra practice. The answers to these questions are on the back of each page.
- A "Glossary of Terms" and a "Table of Measurements" are at the back of the book.
- Adjust the program to vacations, etc. Presentation of mixed concepts on every page ensures that all skills are reinforced; therefore, pages may be completed in any order.
- If your child experiences difficulty with concepts that have been already taught, address the problem with his or her teacher in the fall; more consistent problems indicate that a tutor may be needed.

We appreciate your comments. Please send in the enclosed evaluation page before November 1st, after your child has returned to school in the fall and you are able to determine the success of the Summer Math Skills Sharpener.

Dear Customer,

Every effort has been made to ensure the quality of this product. If any pages are missing or unclear, please call us at 1-800-411-8186 and we will be happy to send replacement pages.

Our commitment is to provide a product that is in keeping with the current standards of the Common Core Curriculum upon which the curricula in schools across the country are based. Please note that states, school systems and schools may differ from one another in what concepts are taught in a particular grade level.

Summer Math Skills Sharpener books may include concepts, terminology, or graphics that appear unfamiliar to parents. Please be advised that everything contained in the books appears in texts and standardized tests used across the nation. Please feel free to call for clarification.

We hope that using the Summer Math Skills Sharpener is a positive experience for your child; however, many children may need a reward system to help them complete the book.

If at any time you are not pleased with the quality of our products, know that we guarantee 100% satisfaction or your money will be refunded within one year of purchase.

Thank you for your order, and again, please feel free to call us at 1-800-411-8186.

Parent Order Form

Phone, Fax and Internet orders placed by 3pm Eastern Time on weekdays, ship the same day. We do not ship on weekends or holidays.

- ***Phone*** credit card orders to **800-411-8186** Monday – Friday, 9 am to 5 pm EST
- ***Fax*** credit card orders to **800-280-9269**
- ***Mail*** orders with check or credit card information to our NEW ADDRESS: Summer Skills • 2921 Wilson Dr. NW • Grand Rapids, MI 49534
- ***Internet*** orders are placed at www.summerskills.com (a secured site.)

We do not sell or share our customer information.

Make checks payable to:
Summer Skills

Billing Address

Name ____________________

Address ____________________

City ______________ **ST**_____ **Zip**________

Phone (_____) _______ - __________

Shipping Address (if different)

Name ____________________

Address ____________________

City ______________ **ST**_____ **Zip**________

Name of Child's school ____________________

Credit Card# (M/C, Visa, AmEx or Discover) ____________________ **Exp** ________ **CCV** ________

Email ____________________

Please indicate the number of **review** books you are ordering:

MATH

____ Pre-K
____ Kindergarten
____ 1st grade
____ 2nd grade
____ 3rd grade
____ 4th grade
____ 5th grade
____ 6th grade
____ 7th grade
____ Basic Math Review for the Middle Grades
____ Prealgebra
____ Algebra 1
____ Geometry
____ High School (Geometry & Algebra II)
____ Math for Life

LANGUAGE ARTS

____ Pre-K
____ Kindergarten
____ 1st grade
____ 2nd grade
____ 3rd grade
____ 4th grade
____ 5th grade
____ 6th grade
____ 7th grade
____ HS Prep

____ **STUDY SKILLS SHARPENER**
(For students 7th Grade through High School.)

____ **SPANISH I REVIEW**
(For students who have completed one full year of Spanish at the middle or high school level.)

____ **SPANISH II REVIEW**
(For students who have completed two full years of Spanish at the middle or high school level.)

____ **FRENCH I REVIEW**
(For students who have completed one full year of French at the middle or high school level.)

____ **TOUCH THE FUTURE**
(Keyboarding for 3rd through 6th grades.)

Make checks payable to:
Summer Skills

Total Number of books ________ x **$18** = ________

Shipping Cost (see chart below) + ________

Total Cost due to Summer Skills = ________

Shipping Chart

To expedite via UPS Air or to ship outside the U.S. call 800-411-8186

Standard Shipping	Media Mail Up to 8 Business Days	Fed Ex **2-3 business days	USPS Priority **3-4 business days	USPS Express Priority **1-2 business days	UPS Ground **2-5 business days
Order Amount					*** call for HI, AK & PR**
1 Book	$3.80	$6.99	$8.00	$26.00	$12.00
2-3 Books	$5.00	$8.20	$9.00	$45.00	$13.50
4-5 Books	$6.00	$8.20	$9.00	$46.00	$14.50
6-10 Books	$8.00	$13.15	$9.00	$60.00	$15.50
11 or more books	not available	please call	please call	please call	please call

*** Orders to HI, AK and Puerto Rico ship USPS Priority Mail. Call for other mailing options.**
**** Orders placed by 3pm EST on weekdays, ship the same day. We do not ship on weekends or holidays.**

To assist in our efforts to comply with changing sales tax laws, please enclose a properly executed sales tax exemption certificate if you are an exempt institution.

GRADE 6 & 7 HELP PAGES

ESTIMATION AND ROUNDING

To estimate means to make a good guess. *Rounding* helps you to estimate more easily.

You can *round* numbers by using place value.

To *round* 362 to the nearest hundred:

1st Step	Find the hundreds place: <u>3</u>62
2nd Step	Look at the digit one place to its <u>right:</u> 3<u>6</u>2
3rd Step	If the digit is 5 or greater, *round* up. If the digit is less than 5, *round* down 6 > 5 so *round* up. To the nearest hundred, 362 *rounds* up to 400.

When you *round* down, the digit in your *rounding* place stays the same.

Example: 334 *rounds* down to 300.

ROUNDING DECIMALS

You can round decimals just as you round whole numbers.

Using place value, find the place you are trying to round to.

Look at the digit one place to its <u>right.</u>

If the digit is 5 or greater, round up. If the digit is less than 5, round down.

After you round a decimal number, you drop the digits to the right of the place you are rounding to.

Example: Round 6.526 to the nearest hundredth.

1st Step	Find the hundredths place: 6.5<u>2</u>7
2nd Step	Look at the place to the right: 6.52<u>7</u>
3rd Step	7 is more than 5 so you round up and drop the 7. To the nearest hundredth 6.527 rounds up to 6.53.

GRADE 6 & 7 HELP PAGES

ADDITION OF LARGE NUMBERS

To add large numbers, it is important to line up the digits according to place value. To make this job easier, line up numbers using *periods.*

Periods

Three places in the place value chart make up a *period. Periods* are always counted from the right (from the ones column) of a number. *Periods* are separated in numerals by commas.

Example: 1 , 0 0 0 (ones period) 1 , 0 0 0, 0 0 0 (thousands period, ones period)

Count three digits from the right, insert commas.

ADDITION WITH REGROUPING (Carrying)

It is a good idea to estimate before computing to see if your answer is reasonable.

Example: 163,597 + 90,443 (Estimate 160,000 + 90,000 = 250,000

1st Step

```
  163,597
+  90,443
---------
```

Put in vertical form. Line up the digits according to place value.

2nd Step	Add the ones. Trade if needed.
3rd Step	Add the tens. Trade if needed.
4th Step	Add the hundreds. Trade if needed.
5th Step	Add the thousands. Trade if needed.
6th Step	Add the ten-thousands. Trade if needed.
7th Step	Add the hundred-thousands.

Problem should look like this:

```
  1  1 1 1
  1 6 3,5 9 7
+   9 0,4 4 3
-------------
  2 5 4,0 4 0
```

The *sum* is 254,040. The answer is in keeping with the estimate 250,000.

GRADE 6 & 7 HELP PAGES

ADDING DECIMALS

Adding with decimals is the same as adding with whole numbers except that it is necessary to use the decimal point to line up the numbers, and a decimal point must appear in the answer.

Example: 3.13 + 3.87

1st Step

```
  3.13
+ 3.87
------
```

Line up decimal points.

2nd Step

```
     1
  3.13
+ 3.87
------
    .0
```

Add the hundredths. Trade if needed.

3rd Step

```
   1 1
  3.13
+ 3.87
------
   .00
```

Add the tenths. Trade if needed.

4th Step

```
   1 1
  3.13
+ 3.87
------
  7.00
```

Add the whole numbers.

SUBTRACTION WITH REGROUPING (Borrowing)

Before subtracting, decide if a trade is necessary. You need to trade if there aren't enough ones, tens, hundreds, etc.

Example: 315,422 - 6,567

1st Step

```
  3 1 5, 4 2 2
-       6, 5 6 7
---------------
```

Put in vertical form. Line up the digits according to place value (see "periods" on previous page)

2nd Step Since 7 > 2, make a trade. Subtract the ones.
3rd Step 6 > 1, make a trade. Subtract the tens.
4th Step 5 > 3, make a trade. Subtract the hundreds.
5th Step 6 > 4, make a trade. Subtract the thousands.
6th Step No trade needed. Subtract the ten thousands. 0 holds the place.
7th Step Subtract the hundred thousands. 0 holds the place.

The problem should look like this:

```
      14 13 11
   0  4  3  1 12
 3 1 5, 4 2 2
-    6, 5 6 7
--------------
 3 0 8, 8 5 5
```

The *difference* is 308,855

GRADE 6 & 7 HELP PAGES

SUBTRACTION AND TRADING WITH CONSECUTIVE ZEROS

Before subtracting, decide if a trade is needed. Sometimes you may need to trade with (borrow from) one or more zeros.

Example: 400 - 273

1st Step	4 0 0 - 2 7 3	Write in vertical form, lining up place values.
2nd Step	3 9 10 ~~4~~ ~~0~~ ~~0~~ - 2 7 3	0 < 3; a trade is needed. You need to trade (borrow) 1 ten from 40 tens. This will leave 39 tens and 10 ones.
3rd Step	3 9 10 ~~4~~ ~~0~~ ~~0~~ - 2 7 3 1 2 7	Subtract.

To subtract with 3 zeros, simply follow the same procedure.

Example:

```
 6  9  9 10
 7, 0  0  0   (7, 0, 0, 0 crossed out)
-5, 8  6  4
-----------
 1, 1  3  6
```

SUBTRACTING DECIMALS

Subtracting decimals is the same as subtracting whole numbers except that it is necessary to use the decimal points to line up the numbers. The decimal point must appear in the answer.

Example: 7.2 - 4.03

1st Step	7.20 ← Add 0 to hold the place. - 4.03 .	Align decimals.
2nd Step	1 1 7.~~2~~0 - 4.03 3.17	Subtract. Trade when necessary.

GRADE 6 & 7 HELP PAGES

MULTIPLICATION OF FOUR-DIGITS BY TWO-DIGITS

Students should know multiplication facts and be able to multiply by one and two-digit multipliers. When multiplying larger numbers, the procedure is the same. Multiply by ones; multiply by tens; then add the partial products.

Example:

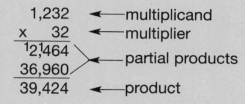

1,232	← multiplicand
x 32	← multiplier
$^{1}2,^{1}464$	← partial products
36,960	
39,424	← product

MULTIPLICATION OF LARGER NUMBERS WITH A THREE-DIGIT MULTIPLIER

Example:

2,366
x 148

2 5 4 2,366 x 148 18,928	<u>Multipy the ones:</u> 8 x 6 = 48, trade the 4 8 x 6 = 48 plus 4 = 52, trade the 5 8 x 3 = 24 plus 5 = 29, trade the 2 8 x 2 = 16 plus 2 = 18, trade the 1
1 2 2 2 5 4 2,366 x 148 18,928 94 640 236 600 350,168	<u>Multipy the tens:</u> 0 is the place holder 4 x 6 = 24, trade the 2 4 x 6 = 24 plus 2 = 26, trade the 2 4 x 3 = 12 + 2 = 14, trade the 1 4 x 2 = 8 + 1 = 9

<u>Multiply the hundreds:</u>
zeros hold the places
1 x 6 = 6
1 x 6 = 6
1 x 3 = 3
1 x 2 = 2

Now add the partial products.

The *product* is 350,168

GRADE 6 & 7 HELP PAGES

MULTIPLYING A DECIMAL BY A DECIMAL

To multiply decimals, treat them as if they were whole numbers, at first ignoring the decimal point.

Example:

1st Step

```
  0.16 ←— multiplicand
x 0.04 ←— multiplier
     ? ←— product
```

2nd Step

```
  0.16
x 0.04
    64
```

Multiply as if the factors were whole numbers.

Then count the places to the right of the decimal point in both the multiplicand and the multiplier. This will give you the number of places to the right of the decimal point needed in the product.

3rd Step

```
0.0064
  4321
```

Add zeros between the decimal point and the product if needed.

Add: 2 places in the multiplicand
+ 2 places in the multiplier
4 places in the product

Count 4 decimal places from the right of the product to place the decimal point.

The *product* is .0064

DIVISION OF FOUR-DIGITS BY TWO-DIGITS

When the dividend and divisor are numbers with two or more digits, division becomes a step-by-step process.

Example:

```
                     ??   ←——— quotient
divisor ——→ 75 ) 2083    ←——— dividend
```

1st Step

Round the divisor up (75 rounds up to 80) and estimate the number of 80's in 208. The answer is 2.

2nd Step

```
      2
75 ) 2083
    -150
```

Multiply the divisor by the quotient (2 x 75) if the product of those two numbers is larger than the dividend, try a smaller quotient.

3rd Step

```
     2
75 /2083
   -150
     58
```

Subtract and compare the remainder and the divisor. If the remainder is greater than the divisor, the quotient tried is too small; try a larger quotient.

4th Step

```
     27
75 /2083
   -150
    583
```

Pull down the next digit from the dividend (3) and repeat the estimation and subtraction process. (How many times can 80 go into 583?) The answer is 7 times.

5th Step

```
     27
75 /2083
   -150
    583
    525
     58
```

Multiply the divisor (7 x 75), subtract the product from the dividend, and compare.

6th Step

75 is larger than 58, so the number left over is called the *remainder.* The *remainder* should be written as a fraction or decimal.

Example: As a fraction

```
     27
75 /2083
   -150
    583
    525
     58
```

$\frac{58}{75}$ → $27\frac{58}{75}$

Use the divisor as the denominator. Always reduce to lowest terms.

Example: As a decimal

```
     27.773
75 /2083.000
   -150
    583
    525
     580
     525
      550
      525
       250
       225
```

27.773 → 27.77

Divide to the thousandths place. Round that number to the hundredths place.

The *quotient* is $27\frac{58}{75}$ or 27.77

DIVIDING DECIMALS

Begin dividing decimals the same way you would divide whole numbers.

Example:

1st Step: $1.5\overline{)6}$ ← dividend; ↗ divisor

2nd Step: $1.5 \times 10 = 15$ (↗ power of ten)

Write the divisor as a whole number. Do this by multiplying the divisor by a power of 10 large enough to make it a whole number.

3rd Step: $6 \times 10 = 60$ (↗ power of ten)

Then multiply the dividend by the same power of 10.

It becomes

$$15\overline{)60}$$
$$\underline{60}$$
$$0$$

4th Step:

$$\begin{array}{r} 4. \\ 15.\overline{)60.} \end{array}$$

← Align decimal points

Now divide.

Another Example: $.036\overline{)7.2}$

$.036 \times 1000 = 36$

$7.2 \times 1000 = 7{,}200$

$$\begin{array}{r} 200. \\ 36.\overline{)7200.} \\ \underline{7200} \\ 0 \end{array}$$

ORDERING DECIMALS

If you know how to compare two decimals, you are then able to put a group of decimals in order.

1st Step

0.322
0.224
0.314

Line up the decimal points.

2nd Step	0.<u>3</u>22 0.<u>2</u>24 0.<u>3</u>14	0.3 > 0.2, so 0.224 is the least.	Begin at the left. Find the first place where the digits are different. Compare.
3rd Step	0.3<u>2</u>2 0.3<u>1</u>4	0.0<u>2</u> > 0.0<u>1</u>, so 0.3<u>2</u>2 > 0.3<u>1</u>4	Compare the remaining digits.
4th Step	Order from least to greatest: 0.224 ⟶ 0.314 ⟶ 0.322		

FRACTIONS

To work with fractions, you must be familiar with the terminology.

FACTORS – Factors are two numbers that when multiplied together form a product.

Example: 3 x 2 = 6

3 (Factor) x 2 (Factor) = 6 (Product)

Every number except 1 has at <u>least</u> two factors: 1 and itself.

Example: 3 has only two factors: 3 and 1
6 has only four factors: 6, 1, 2 and 3

The *common factors* of two numbers are factors that they share.

Example: Common Factors of 6 and 18 (1, 2, 3 and 6)

(1) x (6) = 6
(2) x (3) = 6
(1) x 18 = 18
(2) x 9 = 18
(3) x (6) = 18

The *greatest common factor* of two numbers is the common factor with the highest value.

Example: Find the *greatest common factor* of 12 and 36.

Factors of 12: 1, 2, 3, 4, 6, (12)

Factors of 36: 1, 2, 3, 4, 6, 9, (12), 18, 36

12 is the *greatest common factor*

MULTIPLES

To find the *multiples* of a number, multiply the number by other whole numbers. The list is infinite.

Example:

3 x 1 = 3
3 x 2 = 6
3 x 3 = 9
3 x 4 = 12
and so on

} Multiples of 3.

Some numbers share some of the same multiples. Those multiples are known as *common multiples*.

Example:

Multiples of 2	Multiples of 3
2 x 1 = 2	3 x 1 = 3
2 x 2 = 4	3 x 2 = $\boxed{6}$
2 x 3 = $\boxed{6}$	3 x 3 = 9

6 is a *common multiple* of 2 and 3

If we were to look for more *multiples* of 2 and 3, we could go on forever. Usually, we try to find the *least common multiple* (LCM) or the lowest number in value that is common to both.

Example:

Multiples of 2	Multiples of 3
2 x 1 = 2	3 x 1 = 3
2 x 2 = 4	3 x 2 = $\boxed{6}$
2 x 3 = $\boxed{6}$	3 x 3 = 9
2 x 4 = 8	3 x 4 = $\boxed{12}$
2 x 5 = 10	3 x 5 = 15
2 x 6 = $\boxed{12}$	3 x 6 = 18

The *least common multiple* (LCM) is 6 because it is the lowest number in value of all the multiples of 2 and 3.

GRADE 6 & 7 HELP PAGES

LEAST COMMON DENOMINATOR (LCD)

When fractions have the same denominator it is called a *common denominator*.

To add, subtract or compare fractions, you must first find their *least common denominator*. This is the same as finding the *least common multiple* of the denominators.

Example: We already know that the *least common multiple* of 2 and 3 is 6 (see previous page). Therefore, the *LCD* of $\frac{1}{2}$ and $\frac{2}{3}$ is 6.

Now rewrite the fractions to make the denominators 6.

$\frac{1}{2} = \frac{?}{6}$ $\quad 6 \div 2 = ③$ $\quad \frac{3 \times 1}{3 \times 2} = \frac{3}{6}$

$\frac{2}{3} = \frac{?}{6}$ $\quad 6 \div 3 = ②$ $\quad \frac{2 \times 2}{2 \times 3} = \frac{4}{6}$

The fractions $\frac{3}{6}$ and $\frac{4}{6}$ can now be compared, added or subtracted.

IMPROPER FRACTIONS

When the numerator of a fraction is larger than or equal to the denominator, the fraction is called an *improper fraction.*

The value of an *improper fraction* is always greater than or equal to one.

Examples: $\frac{4}{3}$ $\frac{6}{5}$ $\frac{8}{8}$

Renaming

When solving problems involving fractions, the answer is never expressed as an improper fraction. Whether it be a sum, difference, product or quotient, the answer must be expressed as a whole or mixed number. This is called *renaming.*

Example: $\frac{4}{3} = 1\frac{1}{3}$ $\quad \frac{6}{5} = 1\frac{1}{5}$ $\quad \frac{8}{8} = 1$

If the *improper fraction* is difficult for you to *rename,* simply divide the numerator by the denominator and express the remainder in fraction form.

Example: $\frac{26}{10} = 10\overline{)26}$ → $2\frac{6}{10}$

$$\begin{array}{r} 2\,\frac{6}{10} \\ 10\overline{)26} \\ \underline{20} \\ 6 \end{array}$$

$$2\frac{6}{10} = 2\frac{3}{5}$$

Remember – *always reduce to lowest terms.*

SIMPLIFYING (Reducing) FRACTIONS (To Lowest Terms)

A fraction is in simplest form when its numerator and denominator have no common factor other than 1.

Divide the numerator and denominator by the greatest common factor

Example: $\frac{12}{18}$

Factors of 12: 2, 3, 4, (6)

Factors of 18: 2, 3, (6), 9

6 is the greatest common factor of 12 and 18.

$$\frac{12}{18} = \frac{12 \div \boxed{6}}{18 \div \boxed{6}} = \frac{2}{3}$$

COMPARING FRACTIONS

With Like Denominators

When fractions have the same denominator, compare the numerators.

Example: Compare $\frac{7}{10}$ to $\frac{5}{10}$

$7 > 5$ so $\frac{7}{10} > \frac{5}{10}$

With Unlike Denominators

When comparing fractions that have *unlike denominators,* find the *least common denominator*. Then make equivalent fractions with the same denominator and compare.

Example: $\frac{2}{3}$ compared to $\frac{3}{4}$

1st Step

Multiples of 3: 3, 6, 9, (12) — Find the least common denominator.

Multiples of 4: 4, 8, (12)

The *least common denominator* is 12.

2nd Step

$\frac{2}{3} = \frac{?}{12}$ $\quad 12 \div 3 = \textcircled{4}$ $\quad \frac{4 \times 2}{4 \times 3} = \frac{8}{12}$

$\frac{3}{4} = \frac{?}{12}$ $\quad 12 \div 4 = \textcircled{3}$ $\quad \frac{3 \times 3}{3 \times 4} = \frac{9}{12}$

3rd Step

$\frac{8}{12} < \frac{9}{12}$ so $\frac{2}{3} < \frac{3}{4}$ — Now compare.

Comparing Mixed Numbers

To compare *mixed numbers,* first compare the whole numbers. If they are the same, compare the fractions.

Example: Compare $2\frac{2}{3}$ and $2\frac{3}{4}$

Now compare.

$2\frac{2}{3} < 2\frac{3}{4}$ because $\frac{2}{3} < \frac{3}{4}$ (see above)

GRADE 6 & 7 HELP PAGES

ORDERING FRACTIONS

If you know how to compare two fractions, then you also know how to order them.

Example: Order $\frac{1}{2}$ $\frac{3}{8}$ $\frac{3}{4}$

1st Step: $\frac{1}{2} = \boxed{\frac{4}{8}}$; $\frac{3}{4} = \boxed{\frac{6}{8}}$; $\boxed{\frac{3}{8}}$ — Rewrite the fractions with the same denominators.

2nd Step: $\frac{3}{8} < \frac{4}{8} < \frac{6}{8}$ — Compare the numerators.

so

$\frac{3}{8} < \frac{1}{2} < \frac{3}{4}$

ORDERING MIXED NUMBERS

To order *mixed numbers,* first compare and order the whole numbers. If the whole numbers are the same, compare and order the fractions.

ADDITION OF FRACTIONS

With Like Denominators

When you add fractions, check the denominators. If the fractions have *like* denominators, add the numerators. The denominator stays the same.

Example: $\frac{3}{8} + \frac{1}{8} = \frac{4}{8} \overset{\text{Simplify}}{=} \frac{1}{2}$

With Unlike Denominators

To add fractions with *unlike* denominators you must first make them equivalent. In other words, you must find the *lowest common denominators.*

Example: $\frac{1}{8} + \frac{1}{4}$

1st Step: Write as equivalent fractions with the same denominator

$\frac{1}{8} = \frac{1}{8}$

$+\frac{1}{4} = +\frac{2}{8}$

Now add the fractions

2nd Step: $\frac{3}{8}$ **The *sum* is $\frac{3}{8}$**

ADDING MIXED NUMBERS WITH LIKE DENOMINATORS

ADDITION:

Add the fraction; then add the whole numbers.

Example:

$$\begin{array}{r} 2\frac{3}{4} \\ +\ 2\frac{3}{4} \\ \hline 4\frac{6}{4} \end{array}$$

Rename if needed $5\frac{2}{4}$

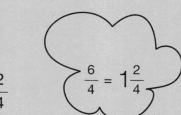

$\frac{6}{4} = 1\frac{2}{4}$

Write in lowest terms

$$5\frac{2}{4} = \boxed{5\frac{1}{2}}$$

ADDING MIXED NUMBERS WITH UNLIKE DENOMINATORS

Example: $2\frac{1}{3} + 3\frac{3}{4}$

1st Step

$$\begin{array}{r} 2\frac{1}{3} = 2\frac{4}{12} \\ +\ 3\frac{3}{4} = 3\frac{9}{12} \\ \hline \end{array}$$

Write equivalent fractions with a common denominator. (See page 13)

2nd Step

$$\begin{array}{r} 2\frac{4}{12} \\ +\ 3\frac{9}{12} \\ \hline 5\frac{13}{12} \end{array}$$

Add the fractions. Add the whole numbers.

Rename if needed $5\frac{13}{12} = 6\frac{1}{12}$

SUBTRACTION OF FRACTIONS USING LIKE DENOMINATORS

Subtract the numerators. The denominator stays the same.

Example: $\frac{5}{8} - \frac{3}{8}$

1st Step

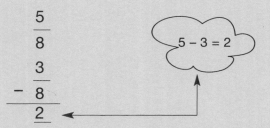

$$\begin{array}{r} \frac{5}{8} \\ -\ \frac{3}{8} \\ \hline 2 \end{array}$$

$5 - 3 = 2$

Subtract the numerators.

2nd Step

$$\begin{array}{r} \frac{5}{8} \\ -\ \frac{3}{8} \\ \hline \frac{2}{8} \end{array}$$

Write the denominator.

3rd Step

$$\frac{2}{8} = \frac{1}{4}$$

Write in lowest terms.

The *difference* is $\frac{1}{4}$

SUBTRACTION OF FRACTIONS WITH UNLIKE DENOMINATORS

Example: $\frac{2}{3} - \frac{1}{9}$

1st Step

$$\begin{array}{rcr} \frac{2}{3} & = & \frac{6}{9} \\ -\ \frac{1}{9} & = & -\ \frac{1}{9} \\ \hline & & \frac{5}{9} \end{array}$$

Write as equivalent fractions with a common denominator. (See page 13)

2nd Step

Now subtract the fractions.

Write in lowest terms if necessary.

GRADE 6 & 7 HELP PAGES

SUBTRACTION OF MIXED NUMBERS WITH LIKE DENOMINATORS

Sometimes you need to make a trade before you subtract with mixed numbers.

1st Step

$$\begin{array}{r} 3\frac{1}{4} \\ -\ \frac{3}{4} \\ \hline \end{array}$$

$\frac{3}{4} > \frac{1}{4}$

Compare the fractions.

2nd Step

$$\begin{array}{r} 3\frac{1}{4} \\ -\ \frac{3}{4} \\ \hline \end{array} \xrightarrow{\text{(trade)}} \begin{array}{r} 2\frac{5}{4} \\ -\ \frac{3}{4} \\ \hline \end{array}$$

Trade (borrow) one whole for $\frac{4}{4}$, and add the $\frac{1}{4}$: $\frac{4}{4} + \frac{1}{4} = \frac{5}{4}$

So: $3\frac{1}{4}$ becomes $2\frac{5}{4}$

3rd Step

$$\begin{array}{r} 2\frac{5}{4} \\ -\ \frac{3}{4} \\ \hline 2\frac{2}{4} \end{array} = 2\frac{1}{2}$$

Subtract fractions. Subtract whole numbers.

Write in lowest terms.

SUBTRACTING A FRACTION FROM A WHOLE NUMBER

Example: $7 - \frac{3}{8}$

1st Step

$$\begin{array}{r} 7 \\ -\ \frac{3}{8} \\ \hline \end{array} \xrightarrow{\text{(trade)}} \begin{array}{r} 6\frac{8}{8} \\ -\ \frac{3}{8} \\ \hline \end{array}$$

Trade (borrow) one whole using same denominator as the fraction. 7 becomes $6\frac{8}{8}$.

2nd Step

$$\begin{array}{r} 6\frac{8}{8} \\ -\ \frac{3}{8} \\ \hline 6\frac{5}{8} \end{array}$$

Subtract fractions. Subtract whole numbers.

Simplify if necessary.

SUBTRACTING MIXED NUMBERS WITH UNLIKE DENOMINATORS

Example: $16\frac{9}{10} - 4\frac{1}{2}$

1st Step

$$\begin{array}{rcr} 16\frac{9}{10} & = & 16\frac{9}{10} \\ -\ 4\frac{1}{2} & = & 4\frac{5}{10} \\ \hline & & 12\frac{4}{10} \end{array}$$

Write equivalent fractions with the same denominator.

2nd Step

Subtract the fractions. Subtract the whole numbers.

3rd Step

$$12\frac{4}{10} = 12\frac{2}{5}$$

Simplify (reduce).

MULTIPLYING FRACTIONS

When multiplying two fractions: Multiply the numerators to find the product's numerator. Multiply the denominators to find the product's denominator.

Example:

$$\frac{1}{2} \times \frac{1}{3} = \frac{1 \times 1}{2 \times 3} = \frac{1}{6}$$

multiply the numerators

multiply the denominators

*It does not matter if the denominators are like or unlike.

MULTIPLYING A MIXED NUMBER BY A FRACTION

To multiply a mixed number by a fraction, change the mixed number to an improper fraction (where the numerator is larger than the denominator), then multiply the fractions.

Example: $1\frac{3}{4} \times \frac{2}{3}$

1st Step: $1\frac{3}{4} = \frac{7}{4}$

Change mixed number to an improper fraction.

(Multiply the whole number by the denominator and add the numerator. This is now the new numerator.) Retain the denominator.

2nd Step: $\frac{7}{4} \times \frac{2}{3} = \frac{14}{}$

Multiply the numerators.

3rd Step: $\frac{7}{4} \times \frac{2}{3} = \frac{14}{12}$

Multiply the denominators.

4th Step: $1\frac{2}{12} = 1\frac{1}{6}$

Rename. Simplify (reduce) the fraction if necessary.

The *product* is $1\frac{1}{6}$

MULTIPLYING TWO MIXED NUMBERS

Follow the same procedure as multiplying a mixed number by a fraction but change both to improper fractions.

Example: $1\frac{1}{2} \times 2\frac{1}{3}$

1st Step: $1\frac{1}{2} = \frac{3}{2}$ $\quad 2\frac{1}{3} = \frac{7}{3}$

Change both mixed numbers to improper fractions.

2nd Step	$\frac{3}{2} \times \frac{7}{3} = \frac{21}{6}$	Multiply numerators. Multiply denominators.
3rd Step	$\frac{21}{6} = 3\frac{3}{6} = 3\frac{1}{2}$	Rename and simplify (reduce).

DIVIDING FRACTIONS

Dividing a Fraction by a Fraction

Example: $\frac{1}{2} \div \frac{1}{3}$

1st Step	$\frac{1}{2} \div \frac{1}{3}$ ← divisor	Locate the *divisor*. In a number sentence, the divisor comes after the division sign.
2nd Step	$\frac{1}{3}$ inverted becomes $\frac{3}{1}$	The divisor must be *inverted*. To *invert* simply means to turn the fraction upside down.
3rd Step	$\frac{1}{2} \times \frac{3}{1} = \frac{3}{2}$	Multiply the two fractions.
4th Step	$\frac{3}{2} = 1\frac{1}{2}$	Rename.

The *quotient* is $1\frac{1}{2}$

Dividing a Whole Number by a Fraction

Example: $2 \div \frac{1}{3}$

1st Step $2 = \frac{2}{1}$ — Put the *whole number* in fraction form.

2nd Step $\frac{2}{1} \div \frac{1}{3}$ ← divisor — Locate the divisor and invert.

$\frac{1}{3}$ becomes $\frac{3}{1}$

3rd Step $\frac{2}{1} \times \frac{3}{1} = \frac{6}{1}$ — Invert the divisor and multiply.

4th Step $\frac{6}{1} = 6$

Dividing a Fraction by a Whole Number

Example: $\frac{1}{3} \div 2$

1st Step $2 = \frac{2}{1}$ — Put the whole number in fraction form.

2nd Step $\frac{1}{3} \div \frac{2}{1}$ ← divisor — Locate the divisor and invert.

$\frac{2}{1}$ becomes $\frac{1}{2}$

3rd Step $\frac{1}{3} \times \frac{1}{2} = \frac{1}{6}$ — Multiply the numerators and denominators.

4th Step $\frac{1}{6}$ is in lowest terms — Simplify (reduce) if necessary.

Dividing a Mixed Number by Another Mixed Number

Example: $2\frac{1}{2} \div 2\frac{1}{4}$

1st Step: $2\frac{1}{2} = \frac{5}{2}$ and $2\frac{1}{4} = \frac{9}{4}$ — Change both mixed numbers to improper fractions.

2nd Step: $\frac{5}{2} \div \frac{9}{4}$ ← divisor — Rewrite the problem. Locate the divisor and invert.

$\frac{9}{4}$ becomes $\frac{4}{9}$

3rd Step: $\frac{5}{2} \times \frac{4}{9} = \frac{20}{18}$ — Multiply the numerators and denominators.

4th Step: $\frac{20}{18} = 1\frac{2}{18} = 1\frac{1}{9}$ — Rename and simplify (reduce).

More About Dividing Fractions:

You know the algorithm for dividing fractions. Let's look at why it works. Consider the problem $\mathbf{20 \div 5}$. You are asking the question, how many groups of 5 are there in 20? $\mathbf{20 \div 5 = 4}$. Answer, there are 4 groups.

Now, look at $\mathbf{1 \div \frac{1}{4}}$. You are asking how many groups of $\frac{1}{4}$ are in 1.

$\mathbf{1 \div \frac{1}{4} = 1 \times 4 = 4}$, but why? If this were a pie and each slice were $\frac{1}{4}$ of the pie, there would be 4 slices.

Suppose only $\frac{1}{2}$ of a pie is left. How many $\frac{1}{4}$ slices would there be?

$\mathbf{\frac{1}{2} \div \frac{1}{4} = \frac{1}{2} \times 4 = 2}$. There are 2 slices.

Consider a pizza cut into eight slices. Each slice is $\frac{1}{8}$ of the pizza. How many slices?

8, of course. Let's say that by the time you reach the pizza, there is only $\frac{1}{4}$ left. How many $\frac{1}{8}$ slices in $\frac{1}{4}$ of a pizza?

$\frac{1}{4} \div \frac{1}{8} = \frac{1}{4} \times 8 = 2$. There are 2 pieces left.

When you multiply a number by a fraction, here is what happens.

$$15 \times \frac{2}{5} = \frac{15 \times 2}{5} = \frac{30}{5} = 6$$

Notice, you multiply by 2, but divide by 5.

When you divide a number by a fraction, you do the opposite.

$12 \div \frac{2}{5} = 12 \div 2 \times 5 = \frac{12 \times 5}{2} = \frac{60}{2} = 30$ Observe, that $12 \div \frac{2}{5} = 12 \times \frac{5}{2}$.

PERCENTAGES

Percentages are ratios. The term *percent* means "one part per hundred."

Example: $30\% = \frac{30}{100}$

Every percent is really a fraction with 100 as its denominator. That also means that every fraction with 100 as its denominator can be written as a percent.

Example: $\frac{30}{100} = 30\%$

Percents can also be expressed as decimals.

Example: 30% = .30

Therefore, there is a relationship among percents, decimals and fractions.

Example: $30\% = .30 = \frac{30}{100}$

$17\% = .17 = \frac{17}{100}$

To Change a Fraction to a Percent

Divide the numerator by the denominator.

Example: $\frac{2}{5} = 5\overline{)2.00}$ = .40

40% — Then change the decimal to a percent.

To Change a Percent to a Fraction

Express it as a fraction and reduce.

Example: 40%

$40\% = \frac{40}{100} = \frac{4}{10} = \frac{2}{5}$

To Compare Fractions, Decimals and Percents

Change them all to decimals.

Example: Put the following in order least to greatest; $\frac{1}{2}$, .25, 35%

1st Step	$\frac{1}{2} = 2\overline{)1.00}$ = .50 35% = .35	Change fraction and percent to decimals.
2nd Step	Now compare; .50 .35 .25	Compare the decimals.
3rd Step	Least to greatest; .25 < .35 < .50 so	Order.
4th Step	$.25 < 35\% < \frac{1}{2}$	Put in original form. Order.

INTRODUCTION OF A VARIABLE IN AN ALGEBRAIC PROBLEM

A *variable* is a quantity that can change.

Example: x and n are two common variables. Their values change according to the problem. In one problem n may stand for the number 3; in another it may stand for the number 53.

An *expression* refers to numbers and variables joined together using the operations of arithmetic.

When solving a word problem use the numbers given to you. Use a variable for numbers **not** given to you. Then write an expression that describes what's going on in the problem.

Example: I had 3 marbles: Bob gave me more marbles.

expression: $3 + n$
n represents the number you don't know.

You can also use a *variable* in other types of problems such as:

Subtraction: $n - 3$
Multiplication: $3n$ (write multiplication without the times (x) symbol.)

Division: $\frac{n}{3}$ (write division in fraction form.)

In each case 3 is the known quantity, and n is the unknown quantity.

When you evaluate an expression, you substitute a number for every variable in that expression. Then you can compute. See the chart below for examples.

Expression	**Evaluate if n = 12**
$n + 3$	$12 + 3 = 15$
$n - 3$	$12 - 3 = 9$
$3n$	$3 \times 12 = 36$
$\frac{n}{3}$	$12 \div 3 = 4$

An *equation* is a mathematical sentence. It always says that two expressions are equal.

When you *solve an equation* you find values for the variables that make the equation true. Sometimes there is only one solution, and sometimes there is more than one solution.

SIMPLE INTEREST FOR ONE YEAR

Money can be borrowed from a lender (bank) for a fee. This fee is called *interest.* The money borrowed is called the *principal* and the *interest rate* is the percentage of interest the bank charges.

To find how much interest you owe for one year, multiply the principal times the interest rate.

Example: Suppose you need to borrow \$5,000 from the bank. If the interest rate is 9%, you can calculate how much you will owe the bank.

(Principal) money borrowed → \$5,000; interest rate → .09; interest amount → \$450.00

\$5,000 x .09 = \$450.00

\$450.00 + \$5,000 = \$5,450 ← The amount of money to be repaid to the bank.

*Interest rates can fluctuate (change) from loan to loan.

ORDER OF OPERATIONS: **Parentheses, powers, multiplication and division, from left to right; addition and subtraction, from left to right. (Use "Pretty Please, My Dear Aunt Sally" to help you remember this.)**

Ex. $(9-1) \div 4 + 2 \times 3^2$

1. **Parentheses:** $8 \div 4 + 2 \times 3^2$
2. **Powers:** $8 \div 4 + 2 \times 9$
3. **Multiplication and division, from left to right:** $2 + 18$
4. **Addition and subtraction, from left to right:** 20

ALGEBRA LANGUAGE:

VARIABLE: **A variable is a letter that can be replaced by a number.**

Ex. $x + 8 = 13$ **The x is a variable. In this case $x = 5$ (x is replaced by 5) makes this a true sentence. A variable can be a part of an expression.**

Ex. $4x$ **The x is the variable. Notice that in this case any value of x is allowed.**

ALGEBRAIC EXPRESSION: **When numbers and variables are joined by the operations of arithmetic, an algebraic expression is formed.**

Ex. $2a + 5$

ALGEBRAIC SENTENCE: **An algebraic sentence occurs when algebraic expressions are joined by a math verb. Math verbs are $=$, $<$, $>$, $\leq$, $\geq$, and $\approx$. Think of writing a math sentence as translating from English language to math language.**

Ex. **Three times a number plus 2 is 15.** $3x + 2 = 15$

The opposite of a number is two times the number. $-x = 2x$

The cost (c) is greater than \$5.00. $c > \$5.00$

EQUATION: **When two expressions are equal, the math sentence is an equation.**

Ex. $5x - 8 = 12$

GRADE 6 & 7 HELP PAGES

SOLVING ALGEBRAIC SENTENCES:

Think of solving an algebraic sentence as "unlocking" it. To do this you will perform opposite or inverse operations.

Ex. 1

$x + 8 = -10$

$+ -8 \quad + -8$ **Add −8 (the opposite of 8) to both sides of the equation.**

$x = -18$

Ex. 2

$2x = \frac{4}{5}$

$\frac{1}{2} \bullet 2x = \frac{4}{5} \bullet \frac{1}{2}$ **Multiply both sides of the equation by $\frac{1}{2}$ (the inverse of 2)**

$x = \frac{2}{5}$

Another name for inverse is *reciprocal.*

Ex. 3

$\frac{1}{2}x - 5 = 8$

$+5 \quad +5$

$\frac{1}{2}x = 13$ **Notice that addition preceded multiplication.**

$2 \bullet \frac{1}{2}x = 13 \bullet 2$

$x = 26$

You might want to think about "unlocking" an equation as performing the order of operations in reverse order.

Ratio, Rate, Proportions, and Means-Extremes Property

Rate: Rate is a quotient. When x and y are quantities in *different units*, then x/y is the amount of x per amount of y. The word "per" means divide.

Ratio: Ratio is a quotient of x and y when they are in the *same units*.

Proportion: When two ratios or two rates are equal, they form a proportion.

Means-extremes: A convenient way to solve a proportion for an unknown number is to use the means-extremes property. It states that if $\frac{a}{b}=\frac{c}{d}$ then $ad = bc$. Your teacher may have called this cross multiplying or cross products.

Ex. 1: Show that $\frac{3}{4}=\frac{9}{12}$

$$4 \times 9 = 3 \times 12$$
$$36 = 36$$

Ex. 2: Solve for x.

$$\frac{3}{20}=\frac{x}{40}$$
$$20x = 120$$
$$\frac{1}{20} \bullet 20x = 120 \bullet \frac{1}{20}$$
$$x = 6$$

Ex. 3: Twenty pounds of cat food costs \$27.80. What is the cost, c, of 25 pounds?

a. Write the rate: $\frac{20 \textit{ pounds}}{27.80}$

b. Write the proportion and solve:

$$\frac{20 \textit{ pounds}}{\$27.80}=\frac{25 \textit{ pounds}}{c}$$
$$25 \times \$27.80 = 20c$$
$$\frac{1}{20} \times 25 \times \$27.80 = 20c \times \frac{1}{20}$$
$$\$34.75 = c$$

More with rate

Suppose you have a rate in one unit and you wish to convert it to another.

Consider: You read an average of 25 pages every day. How many will you read in a month? (Use 1 month = 30 days)

$$\frac{25\ pages}{day} \times \frac{30\ days}{month} = \frac{750\ pages}{month}$$

Statistics:

A statistical question is one for which there are a variety of answers. The collected data can be described by its center and by its spread.

Measures of Central Tendency: There are three measures of central tendency: the *mean*, the *median*, and the *mode*.

Consider the data values 3 3 6 7 8 8 11 12 14

Mean: The mean is the average of a set of data.

$$mean = \frac{sum\ of\ data\ values}{number\ of\ data\ values}$$

$$mean = \frac{3+3+6+7+8+8+11+12+14}{9} = 8$$

Median: The median is the number in the middle when the values are ordered from smallest to largest. If there is an even number of data values, it is the average of the two in the middle. In the case above, the median is 8.

Mode: This is the number that occurs the most often. The data set has two modes, 3 and 8.

Statistics continued:

Mean absolute distribution (MAD): This is the average of how much data values differ from the mean value. A small MAD shows that data values are near the mean. A large MAD shows a wide spread of data. Here is how you find it.

In the example set , the mean is 8. Find the deviation (absolute distance) of each point from the mean.

$8-3=5,\quad 8-3=5,\quad 8-6=2,\quad 8-7=1,\quad 8-8=0,\quad 8-8=0$

$11-8=3\quad 12-8=4\quad 14-8=6$

The numbers 5, 5, 2, 1, 0, 0, 3, 4, and 6 represent the deviation of each number from the mean.

$$\text{The } MAD = \frac{sum\ of\ deviations\ from\ mean}{number\ of\ data\ values}$$

$$MAD = \frac{5+5+2+1+0+0+3+4+6}{9} = 2.\overline{8}$$

For this data set, the average spread from a mean of 8 is $2.\overline{8}$.

Interquartile range (IQR): Another measure of spread is the interquartile range. This is used with the median and is a measure of the middle 50% of the data. To find it, use the following steps:

We know the median is 8. The lower quartile is the median of the data values to the left of 8. In this case it is $\frac{3+6}{2}=4.5$. The upper quartile is the median of the data values to the right of 8. $\frac{11+12}{2}=11.5$. IQR = upper quartile – lower quartile. IQR = 11.5 – 4.5 = 7.

PLACE VALUE CHART

3,679,164,523,678.396528316546

6	trillionths (.000000000006)
4	hundred billionths (.00000000004)
5	ten billionths (.0000000005)
6	billionths (.000000006)
1	hundred millionths (.00000001)
3	ten millionths (.0000003)
8	millionths (.000008)
2	hundred thousandths (.00002)
5	ten thousandths (.0005)
6	thousandths (.006)
9	hundredths (.09)
3	tenths (.3)
.	
8	ones (8)
7	tens (70)
6	hundreds (600)
,	
3	thousands (3,000)
2	ten thousands (20,000)
5	hundred thousands (500,000)
,	
4	millions (4,000,000)
6	ten millions (60,000,000)
1	hundred millions (100,000,000)
,	
9	billions (9,000,000,000)
7	ten billions (70,000,000,000)
6	hundred billions (600,000,000,000)
,	
3	trillions (3,000,000,000,000)

Lesson #1

1. Evaluate and simplify:

a. $2\frac{1}{2} + 3\frac{3}{4}$ = ______

b. $1\frac{2}{3} + 6\frac{5}{6}$ = ______

c. $2\frac{11}{12} + \frac{5}{6}$ = ______

2. Rename each of the following as a decimal:

a. $\frac{1}{4}$ ________ b. $\frac{3}{4}$ ________ c. $\frac{2}{5}$ ________

d. $\frac{1}{3}$ ________ e. $\frac{7}{10}$ ________ f. $\frac{1}{2}$ ________

3. $\frac{9}{15} \times \frac{15}{18} =$ __________

4. Simplify: (Review the order of operations from the "Help Pages.")

a. $-3 + 3 =$ ________ b. $18 \div 3 \times 2 =$ ________ c. $3^2 - 3 \div 3 =$ ________

5. Lana has a friend who is deaf and uses sign language to communicate. She can sign about 36 concepts per minute. How many concepts can she sign in a 15 minute period?

____

6. A *ratio* is the quotient of two quantities in the same unit. Grandma's chewy brownie recipe uses 2 cups of sugar and 3 cups of flour for one full recipe.

a. What is the ratio of sugar to flour? __________

b. If you have 5 cups of sugar, how many cups of flour will you need? __________

7. $.09\overline{)83.88}$

8. A *variable* is a symbol that can be replaced by a number. Let $x = 3$ and $y = -2$, find:

a. $x + y$ ________ b. $x - y$ ________ c. xy ________

d. x^2 ________ e. $\frac{x}{y}$ ________ f. y^2 ________

9. Identify the ordered pairs on this graph.

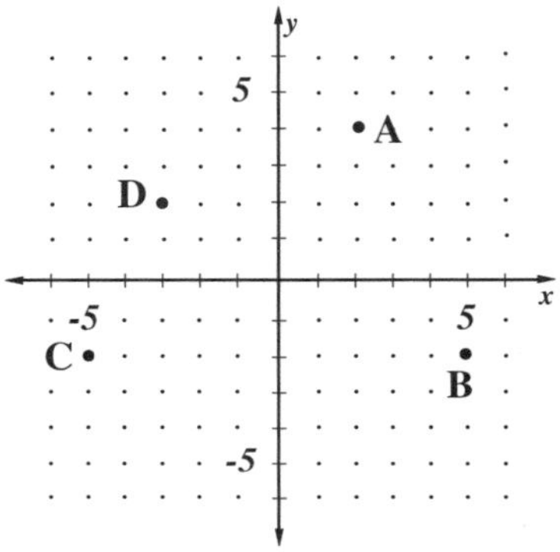

A = ________ B = ________

C = ________ D = ________

10. If you spin this wheel, which letter has:

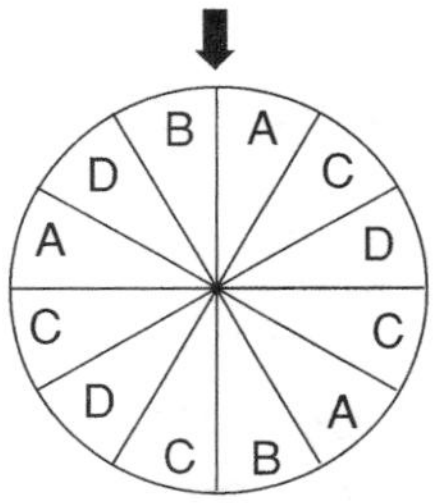

a. the best chance of appearing? ________

b. the least chance of appearing? ________

11. Mental math: .1 divided by 100 = ________

12. Suppose gold sells for $924.50 an ounce. With a calculator find the following.

a. A friend weighs 100 pounds, what is her worth in gold? ________

b. What is your worth in gold? ________

Lesson #2

1. What percent of $5.00 is 3 quarters, 3 dimes and 4 nickels? ________

2. Evaluate and simplify:

a. $3\frac{3}{4} - 1\frac{1}{2}$ = ______

b. $2\frac{3}{8} - 1\frac{3}{4}$ = ______

c. $9\frac{1}{8} - 3\frac{1}{2}$ = ______

3. Complete the table.

2^0 ______	2^1 ______	2^2 ______	2^3 ______
2^4 ______	2^5 ______	2^6 ______	2^7 ______
2^8 ______	2^9 ______	2^{10} ______	

4. Mental math: $\frac{5}{6} + \frac{1}{3} =$ ________

5. $2\frac{1}{2}$ gallons = ________ quarts = ________ pints

6. *Percent* means per centum or per 100. It is a ratio of a number to 100. When you see "per" think "division." Rename each of the following as a percent:

a. $\frac{1}{2}$ ________ b. .8 ________ c. .08 ________

d. $\frac{3}{5}$ ________ e. $\frac{33}{100}$ ________ f. 1 ________

7. Estimate this product: 419 x 97 = __________

8. Put in order from least to greatest:

3^2 100 ÷ 10 $\frac{77}{11}$ 8% of 100

__________ __________ __________ __________

9. Fifty students were surveyed as to what kind of pizza they preferred. Thirty-six chose pepperoni pizza.

a. Write the ratio of students who like pepperoni pizza to students surveyed.

____

b. If pizza were offered to a school of 500, how many would you expect to choose pepperoni?

____

10. A *formula* is an equation stating that a single variable is equal to an expression. The formula for the area, A, of a rectangle with length, l, and width, w, is $A = lw$. Find the area of a rectangle with $l = 2\frac{1}{2}$ feet and $w = 3\frac{3}{4}$ feet. __________

11. A *multiple* of an integer is the product of the number and any nonzero number. A *factor* of a nonzero integer is a number that divides into the integer with no remainder.

a. Name 3 common multiples of 3 and 5. __________, __________, __________

b. Name 3 factors of 30. __________, __________, __________

c. Write the prime integers between 10 and 25. ______________________________

12. Calculator skill: With a calculator find 106% of $2,864. __________

Lesson #3

1. Calculator skill: You have just won a prize that pays you $1 for the first day, $2 for the second day, $3 for the third day and so on for the month of August. How much money did you win?

____

2. Evaluate and simplify:

a. $2\frac{1}{2} \times 3 =$ ________ b. $1\frac{3}{4} \times \frac{1}{7} =$ ________ c. $\frac{2}{3} \times \frac{3}{5} \times \frac{2}{9} =$ ________

3. Write the place value of the underlined digit. .457<u>8</u>1 __________

4. Mental math: 75 x 10,000 = __________

5. Beginning with $\frac{3}{4}$, count to $2\frac{5}{12}$ by $\frac{1}{3}$'s.

$\frac{3}{4}$ $1\frac{1}{12}$ __________ $1\frac{3}{4}$ __________ $2\frac{5}{12}$

6. Convert: 8 miles/hour to feet/minute. __________

7. The formula for the area, A, of a square with side, s, is $A = s^2$. Find the area of a square with: $s = \frac{2}{3}$ in. __________

8. A nickel is what percent of a:

a. dollar? __________ b. quarter? __________

c. dime? __________ d. half-dollar? __________

9. $37\overline{)5,217}$

10. An *arithmetic sequence* is a number pattern where the difference between consecutive numbers (*terms*) is constant.
The first three terms of a sequence are 10, 13, 16 …

a. Find the next two terms in the sequence. __________, __________

b. Using the sequence above, find the difference between two consecutive terms (next and previous).__________ This is the *constant difference* or the *constant rate of change*.

c. If the tenth term is 37, what is the eleventh term? __________

11. Tonya's dog weighs 32 lbs. Her cat weighs 1/2 of what her dog weighs. Her parrot weighs 1/4 of what her cat weighs. How much does her parrot weigh?

____

12. Put these numbers in order from least to greatest:

$\frac{1}{3}$ 30% .3333 $\frac{33}{100}$

__________ __________ __________ __________

Lesson #4

1. a. $7\frac{1}{6} - 3\frac{1}{2} =$ ________ b. $5\frac{1}{4} \div 3\frac{1}{2} =$ ________

2. $.7\overline{)77.7}$

3. Evaluate and simplify:

a. $1\frac{2}{3} \div \frac{5}{6} =$ ________ b. $4\frac{1}{2} \div 2\frac{3}{4} =$ ________ c. $-\frac{4}{9} \div \frac{2}{3} =$ ________

4. Mental math: $4\frac{2}{5} + 3\frac{4}{5} =$ ________

5. Use <, >, or = to make each math sentence true.

a. 3 + 5 x 2 ________ 5 x 3 + 2 b. 5 x 5 - 3 ________ 5 x (5 - 3)

c. 10 - 2 x 5 ________ 2 x 5 - 10 d. 5 - (5 + 5) ________ 5 - 5 + 5

6. The formula for the area, A, of a triangle with base, b, and height, h, is $A = \frac{1}{2}bh$. Find the area of ΔABC pictured at the right.

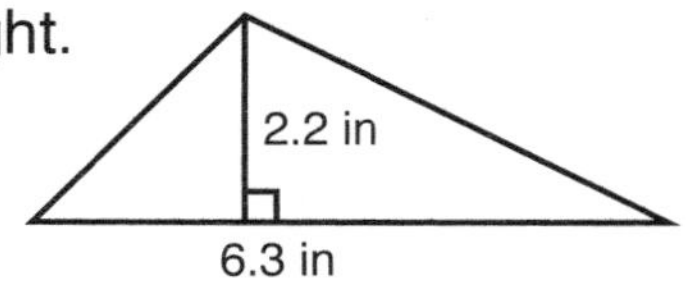

____

7. What is the area of the shaded rectangle?

____

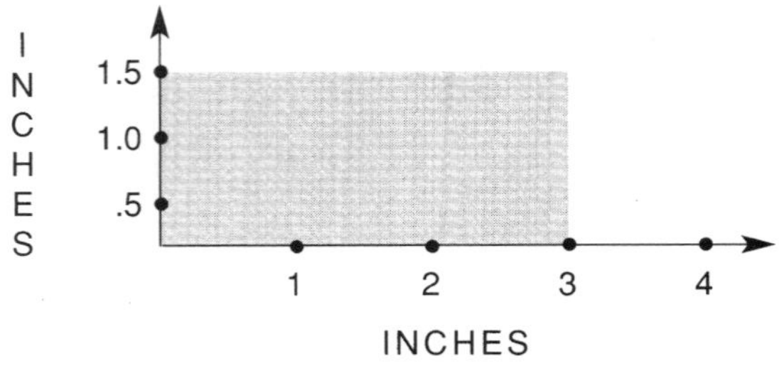

8. When two ratios or rates are equal, they form a *proportion.* The *means-extremes* method, also called *cross multiplying*, can be used to solve a proportion. (Review *means-extremes method* in the "Help Pages.") One hundred nautical miles equals about 115 standard miles. If you travel 1,050 nautical miles, how far have you traveled in standard miles?

a. Write a proportion to represent this situation. _______________

b. Solve your proportion. _______________

9. Put in 2 addition signs between the correct numbers to make this equation true.

5 0 1 0 2 2 5 = 177

10. Evaluate the following:

a. $4 \times \frac{1}{4} =$ __________

b. $-\frac{1}{3} \times -3 =$ __________

c. $\left(\frac{2}{3}\right)\left(\frac{3}{2}\right) =$ __________

d. $\frac{1}{n} \times n =$ __________

e. Generalize: a number times its reciprocal is __________

11. Mental math: $9\frac{3}{4} - 2\frac{1}{2} =$ _________

Lesson #5

1. a. $\frac{3}{4} + \square = 1\frac{1}{4}$ b. $1\frac{1}{2} - \square = 1\frac{1}{4}$

2. $7.6\overline{)630.8}$

3. Round to the nearest tenth: 0.75 __________

4. Circle the number closest in value to 4/5.

a. $\frac{30}{60}$ b. .82 c. 45% of 100

5. Suppose the exchange rate for US dollars to European euros is $1.27 per euro.

a. How many euros would you receive for $40? (Round to the nearest hundredth.)

____

b. Your meal in a fancy Paris restaurant costs 28 euros. What is the cost in US dollars?

____

6. You have a container of cards that are numbered from 1 to 100. If you pick a card at random, what is the probability that the card would be:

a. divisible by 5? _________ b. divisible by 20? __________

Lesson #5 (continued)

7. Sound travels about 1,100 feet per second. About how many miles away is lightning if 10 seconds pass from the time you see the lightning until you hear the thunder?

____

8. The formula for area, A, of a circle with radius, r, is $A = \pi r^2$. Find the area of a circle with r = 4.8 cm. Use π = 3.14. Round to the nearest tenth.

____

9. a. Find three pairs of numbers that satisfy $y = 2x$.

b. Plot these points on the graph at the right and draw a line through them.

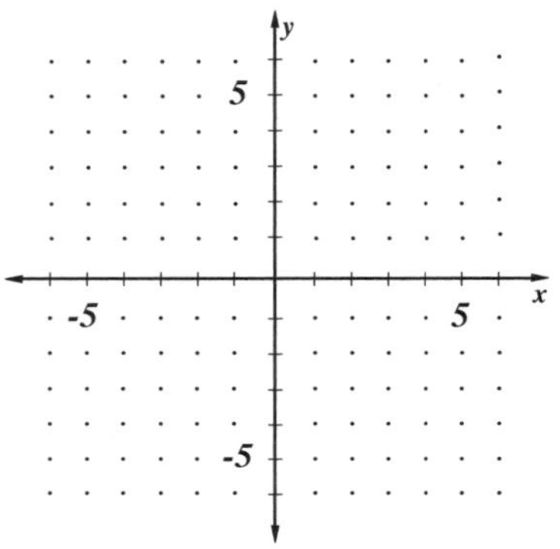

c. The *slope* or *constant rate of change* of a linear equation is the ratio of "rise/run." Pick a point on the line and then, reading from left to right, find the rise and the run to get to the next point.

____

10. Find the prime factors of the following:

a. 9 ________ b. 18 ________ c. 36 ________

d. What is the lowest common multiple of 9, 18, and 36? ______________

11. Tell whether or not each proportion below is true.

a. $\frac{25}{80} = \frac{10}{32}$ ________ b. $\frac{18}{48} = \frac{15}{40}$ ________ c. $\frac{2}{3} = \frac{10}{16}$ ________

Lesson #6

1. a. $\begin{array}{r} 632 \\ \times\ 500 \\ \hline \end{array}$

   b. $\begin{array}{r} 2.34 \\ \times\ .003 \\ \hline \end{array}$

2. a. $4\frac{5}{8} + 3\frac{1}{\square} = 8\frac{1}{8}$

   b. $\frac{\square}{4} - \frac{2}{3} = \frac{1}{12}$

3. If the length of a room is 18 feet, how long should it be on a scale drawing where 1 in. = 2 ft.?

   ____

4. What is the greatest common divisor of these 3 numbers?

   75 125 50

   ____

5. Mental math: Halve these numbers.

   a. 510 __________ b. 1,080 __________ c. 860 __________

6. Mental math: 500 - 50 + 40 - 30 + 3 = __________

7. $6 + (-5) + (-7) =$ __________

8. 32 liters = __________milliliters.

9. Round 1,936,743 to the nearest:

a. 10,000 __________ b. 100,000 __________ c. 1,000,000 __________

10. a. $1\frac{4}{5} \times 1\frac{2}{3} =$ __________ b. $\frac{2}{3} \div \frac{8}{9} =$ __________

11. When Anton learned to read Braille, he read 12 words per minute. Six weeks later he could read 50% faster. Two months later, he increased his speed by 50% again. How many words per minute could he read?

____

12. Mental math: Estimate the product of the problem below by putting the decimal point in the correct place. Check with a calculator.

10.761 x 3.456 = 37190016

____

Lesson #7

1. a. $3\frac{1}{7} \div 5\frac{1}{2} =$ ________ b. $2\frac{2}{3} \times 3\frac{1}{8} =$ ________

2. The formula for the area, A, of a parallelogram with base, b, and height, h, is $A = bh$. Use the parallelogram pictured at the right.

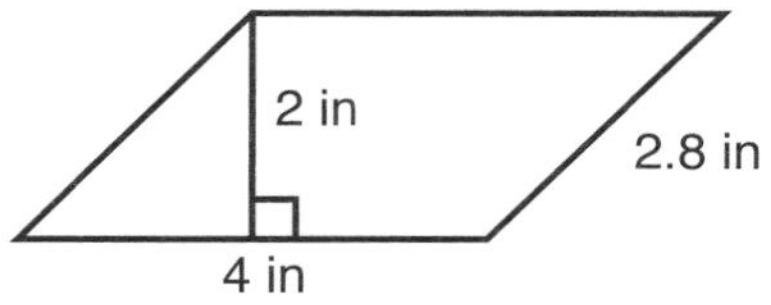

a. Find the perimeter. ________

b. Find the area. ________

3. Mental math: What is 20% of $30.00? ________

4.

```
  7 3, □ □ 1
– 2 7, 8 9 4
  4 5, 1 0 7
```

5. $50.7 \overline{)1{,}662.96}$

6. Put the numbers in order from least to greatest:

-3 -5 $\frac{2}{3}$ -7 $\frac{3}{4}$ $-\frac{1}{6}$

________ ________ ________ ________ ________ ________

Lesson #7 (continued)

7. What percent of $\frac{1}{2}$ is $\frac{1}{4}$? __________

8. A candy bar has 350 calories. 80% of the calories come from fat. How many calories are from fat?

____

9. Round to the nearest hundredth: .773 __________

10. A certain drug was tested on a sample of 1,000 people. Of the group, 800 experienced a positive result.

a. Write the positive result as a percent of the sample. __________

b. If 200,000 people eventually take this drug, how many might you expect to have a positive outcome?

____

11. Amanda babysits to earn extra money. She is paid $5.00 per hour.

a. Complete the table to show her wage, w, for hours, h, worked.

$h = 0$	1	2	3	4	5	h
$w = 0$	$5.00					

b. Write an equation for her wage, w, in terms of hours, h. ______________

c. For five days Amanda babysat for a family six hours each day. How much did she make?

____

Lesson #8

1. Mental math: $4\frac{1}{3} + 1\frac{2}{3} =$ ________

2. a. $1\frac{7}{8} \times 2\frac{2}{5} =$ ________ b. $\frac{3}{4} \div \frac{1}{8} =$ ________

3. Write this number in expanded form: 4,006,080

Example: 1,111 = 1,000 + 100 + 10 + 1

____

4. a. $12\overline{)\$414.72}$ b. $$\begin{array}{r} 12.85 \\ \times\ 0.34 \\ \hline \end{array}$$

5. Write the prime factors of the following:

a. 6 b. 10 c. 20

d. What is the least common multiple of 6, 10, and 20? ____________

6. Put in order from least to greatest:

$-\frac{1}{3}$ $\frac{2}{5}$ $-\frac{1}{4}$ $\frac{2}{3}$ $\frac{5}{6}$ $\frac{5}{8}$

_____ _____ _____ _____ _____ _____

7. Mrs. Whitney surveyed her class as to the number of pets per family. She used the *frequency graph* below to record the results.

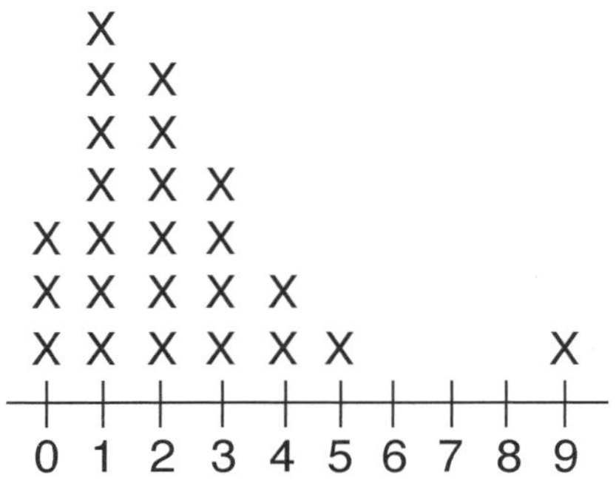

a. How many families did not own a pet? __________

b. What is the median number of pets per family? __________

c. How many families had 3 or more pets? __________

8. Fill in the missing numbers in this time sequence:

1:46 1:57 ___________ 2:19 __________

9. 10,000 lbs = ____________ tons

10. What is 150% of 800? ____________

11. Karl borrowed $5,700 from the bank for a year at 9% simple interest. What was the amount he paid back to the bank? ($I = prt$ where p = principle, r = rate as a percent and t = time.)

____

12. Calculator skill: The sun is approximately 93,000,000 miles from earth. Light travels 186,000 miles per second. How long does it take the light from the sun to reach the earth? (Give your answer in minutes.)

____

1. Simplify:

a. $-\frac{3}{4} + \frac{3}{4} \times \frac{2}{3} =$ ________ b. $\left(\frac{3}{8}\right)\left(-\frac{4}{5}\right) \div \frac{1}{2} =$ ________ c. $\left(\frac{2}{3}\right)^2 \times \frac{1}{4} =$ ________

2. Write an addition problem in which three identical addends combine to equal 12.6.

________ + ________ + ________ = 12.6

3. 300,000 cm = ________ m = ________ km

4. a. $\frac{2}{5} \div \frac{4}{5} =$ ________ b. $2\frac{1}{3} - 1\frac{1}{2} =$ ________

5. What is the largest two-digit prime number? ____

6. Complete the following table:

10^{-3} ________	10^{-2} ________	10^{-1} ________	10^{0} ________
10^{1} ________	10^{2} ________	10^{3} ________	10^{4} ________
10^{5} ________	10^{6} ________		

Lesson #9 (continued)

7. The slope, m, between two points (x_1, y_1) and (x_2, y_2) is $m = \frac{y_2 - y_1}{x_2 - x_1}$.

Find the slope between points (1, 3) and (3, 8). ____________________

8. A *math sentence* is formed when two expressions are joined by a *math verb*. Some math verbs are: $=$, $<$, $>$, $\leq$, $\geq$, $\neq$, and $\cong$.

Translate each of the following into a math sentence. Let n = number.

a. Twice a number is greater than the number plus 8. ____________________

b. 42% of a number is 168. ____________________

c. The difference between a number and 5 is less than 2. ____________________

9. Use the property of reciprocals to solve for x.

a. $3x = \frac{1}{3}$ __________ b. $\frac{3}{4}x = 15$ __________ c. $-\frac{1}{2}x = -3.2$ __________

10. Pete is hiking a $7\frac{1}{2}$ mile trail. He plans to rest every $2\frac{1}{4}$ miles. How many rests will he take? ____________

11. Find the prime factorization of the following:

a. 10 ____________ b. 15 ____________ c. 25 ____________

d. What is the least common multiple of 10, 15, and 25? ____________

Lesson #10

1. a. $400\overline{)8,934}$ b. $.03\overline{)9.012}$

2. Mental math: Solve the following problems by moving the decimal to the right or left. Example: 3,456 ÷ 1,000 = 3.456

a. .32 x 100 ___________ b. 54,793.6 ÷ 1,000 ___________

c. .578629 x 10,000 ___________

3. Write in words: 483,552 ____

4. Two rectangles are similar. One is 25 cm wide and 40 cm long. The other is 60 cm wide and x cm long. Find the length of the second rectangle.

____

5. Your class measured the diameters and circumferences of a variety of circles with the following results:

circumferences	diameters
4.75 in	1.5 in
6.25 in	2 in
12.5 in	4 in
11 in	3.5 in

a. Divide each circumference by its diameter and record your results to the nearest hundredth.

________________ ________________ ________________ ________________

b. Find the average of the four quotients. ______________________

c. Use π = 3.14 to generalize. π is the ratio of ________________ to _______________

6. Mental math: $8 - 4\frac{3}{8} =$ ________

7. Construct or draw the perpendicular bisector of $\overline{CD}$.

8. Which set contains only multiples of seven?

a. 42, 57, 77 b. 37, 49, 63 c. 28, 35, 56 ________

9. Joanie is making dog scarves. Each scarf uses $\frac{3}{8}$ yard of fabric. She has $3\frac{1}{2}$ yards of fabric. How many scarves can she make?

____

10. Mr. Kim paid $360 in interest in one year for his $4,000 car loan. Using the formula for simple interest, what was the rate of interest?

________ %

11. Order these numbers from least to greatest:

.300 $33\frac{1}{3}$ % .33 .303 .334

________ ________ ________ ________ ________

Lesson #11

1. What fraction of the day would you spend in bed if you slept:

a. 8 hours ________ b. 9 hours ________ c. 10 hours ________

2. a. $\frac{1}{9} \times \frac{3}{10} =$ ________ b. $\frac{1}{9} \div \frac{1}{3} =$ ________

3. Complete the table. These are all perfect squares.

1^2 ________	2^2 ________	3^2 ________	4^2 ________
5^2 ________	6^2 ________	7^2 ________	8^2 ________
9^2 ________	10^2 ________	11^2 ________	12^2 ________

4. The formula for the area, A, of a trapezoid with height, h, and bases (b_1 and b_2) is $A = \frac{1}{2}h(b_1 + b_2)$. Use the trapezoid pictured below.

a. Find the perimeter. ________

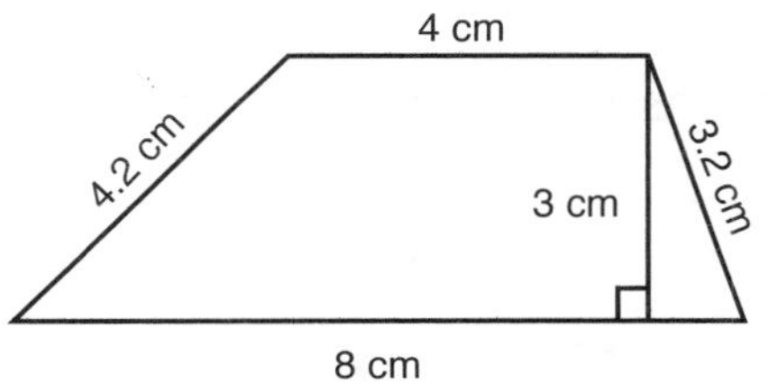

b. Find the area. ________

5. Solve for x:

a. $2x - 3 = -9$ ________ b. $\frac{1}{2}x + \frac{2}{3} = \frac{5}{6}$ ________ c. $-x + 3 = -2$ ________

6. The starting five players for tonight's basketball game are to be introduced. In how many different ways can they be announced?

____

7. Mr. Bennett used the stem-and-leaf graph to display the class' test results.

1	
2	
3	
4	2
5	
6	1 2 5 6
7	2 3 4 7 7 8 8
8	2 3 5 5 5 7 8 8
9	3 5 7 9 9
10	0 0

Key – 7/2 = 72

a. How many students took the test? ______________

b. What was the range of the scores? ______________

c. What was the highest score? ______________

d. What was the lowest score? ______________

e. What was the median score? ______________

f. If a 94 or better was an A, How many A's were there? ______________

8. Construct or draw the bisector of $\angle ABC$.

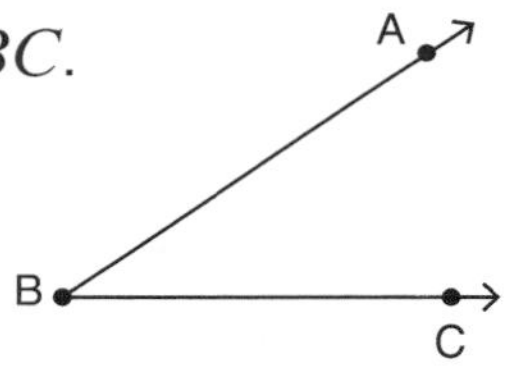

9. Marcos hiked for $5\frac{1}{2}$ miles, rested, hiked another $1\frac{3}{4}$ miles, rested, and then hiked the final x miles. Altogether he hiked 9 miles.

a. Write a math equation to represent this situation. ______________

b. Find x. ______________

10. Write an expression for each of the following: (Let n = number.)

a. twice a number minus 5 ______________________

b. the opposite of a number ______________________

c. number cubed minus 5 ______________________

Lesson #12

1. What number comes next in this sequence?

3 9 27 81 ________

2. Find the square root of each of the following:

a. $\sqrt{25}$ ________ b. $\sqrt{36}$ ________ c. $\sqrt{\frac{1}{4}}$ ________ d. $\sqrt{\frac{25}{36}}$ ________

e. The $\sqrt{30}$ is between $\sqrt{\square}$ and $\sqrt{\square}$. Therefore, it is between

________ and ________

3. In many states the first two symbols on a license plate must be letters. The letters "I" and "O" cannot be used.

a. How many ways can the first two letters on a plate be arranged? ________

b. If the third symbol must be a digit, how many ways can the first three symbols be arranged?

____

4. Apples cost $2.28 for a 3-pound bag.

a. What is the *unit price* (price for one pound)? ________

b. How much would you expect to pay for a 10-pound bag? ________

5. <u>Estimate</u> the difference by rounding to the nearest hundred thousand:

793,112 – 314,349 = ________

6. Name the figure represented by each net.

a. 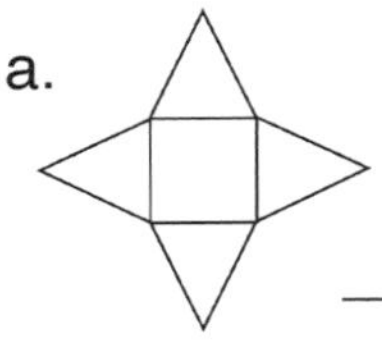 ____________

b. 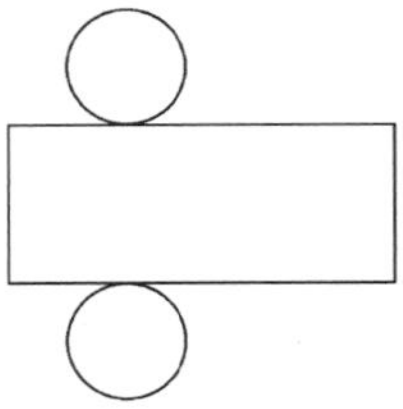 ____________

c. 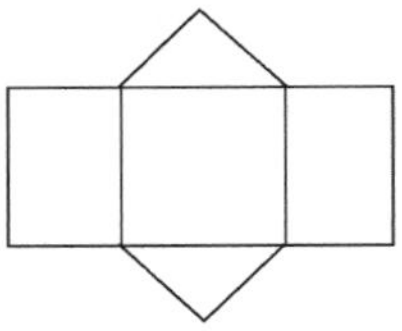 ____________

7. The formula for the volume, V, of a sphere with radius, r, is $V = \frac{4}{3}\pi r^3$. Find the volume of a sphere with $r = 7$ in. Use $\pi = 3.14$ and round to the nearest hundredth.

____

8. Write in exponential form.

a. $x \bullet x \bullet x \bullet x$ ____________

b. 3 x 3 x 3 x 3 x 3 ____________

c. 2 x y x y ____________

d. $\left(\frac{1}{2}\right)\left(\frac{1}{2}\right)\left(\frac{1}{2}\right)\left(\frac{1}{2}\right)$ ____________

9. Circle how many 1,000's make 6,000,000:

a. 600 b. 60,000 c. 6,000 d. 60

10. Pamela has 5 hours to use the computer lab. If each of her programs takes 12 minutes to run, how many programs can she complete?

____

11. Calculator skill: Find out how many hours you have spent in school so far, beginning with first grade. Assume you spend $6\frac{1}{2}$ hours in school each day. Assume that there are 180 school days in each year.

____

Lesson #13

1. A *polynomial* is an expression written as the sum or difference of terms. *Like terms* have the same variables to the same power. Simplify the following polynomials:

a. $3a + 2b + 8a$ ______________

b. $3x^2 - x^2 + x + 1$ ______________

2. $.82\overline{).6724}$

3. Write this number in standard form: eight hundred twenty-one million.

____

4. Unit cost (cost per unit) is an example of a *rate*. If an 18.8 oz. can of chunky soup costs $1.49, find the rate, or cost per ounce. Round to the nearest hundredth.

____

5. 15 is what percent, p, of 75? ______________

6. Cheryl, Carolyn, Linda and Kathy were in line for concert tickets. Cheryl was between Carolyn and Linda. Kathy was not first in line. Carolyn was between Kathy and Cheryl. Put them in the correct order from first to last.

__________ __________ __________ __________

7. Simplify the following:

a. $(8-3)^2 - 4 \times 2 =$ ________ b. $20 \div 2 \times 2^2 =$ ________ c. $3-(-8) =$ ________

8. Mental math:

a. $323 \times 100 =$ ________ b. $63{,}600 \div 100 =$ ________

9. The first term in a sequence is -3 and the fifth term is 17. What is the third term?

____

10. Arrange these decimals in order from least to greatest:

.041 .014 .004 .001

________ ________ ________ ________

11. Willie spent $10 on Monday. On Tuesday he spent 1/2 of what he spent on Monday. On Wednesday he spent 1/5 of what he spent on Monday. How much did he spend altogether in the 3 days?

____

12. The *absolute value* of a number is its positive distance from zero. Find each of the following:

a. $|-6|$ ________ b. $|-16|$ ________ c. $|-25|$ ________

Lesson #14

1. Circle which is more:

a. 20% of a millennium b. a century and a half

2. a. $1\frac{1}{5} \times 2\frac{1}{3} =$ ________ b. $2\frac{1}{6} \div 3\frac{1}{3} =$ ________

3. Consider the polynomial: $5x^4 + 2x^2 + 8$

a. How many terms are in this expression? ______________

b. What is the coefficient of x^2 ? ______________

c. What is the degree of this polynomial? ______________

d. What is the constant? ______________

4. $18\overline{)1{,}234}$

5. One out of four Blue Spruce trees has a blue hue.

a. Write one out of four as a percent. ______________

b. Write one out of four as a ratio. __________

c. On a certain tree farm 2,000 Blue Spruce have been planted.

Approximately how many can be expected to have a blue hue? __________

6. On the wheel to the right:

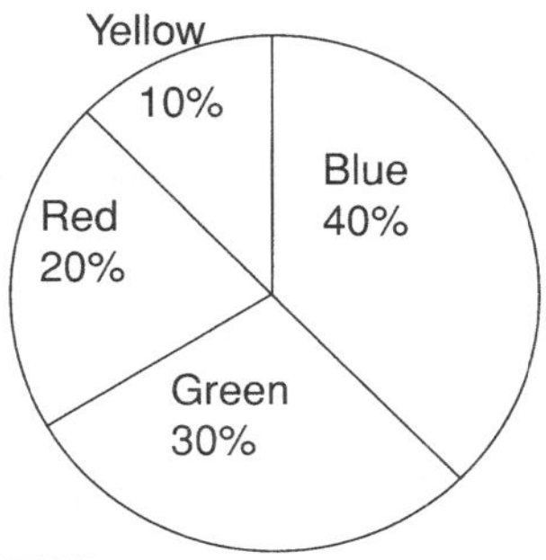

a. What color is 4 times more popular than another?

____

b. What color is 2/3 as popular as another? ________________

Lesson #14 (continued)

7. Garrett has a model railroad built to N scale. N scale is $^1/_{160}$ of actual length. His engine is 4.5 inches long. What is the size of the actual engine? Rename your answer in feet.

____

8. a. Accurately draw ΔABC, where AB = 1 inch, BC = 2 inches, and m$\angle B$ = 45°

b. Explain why all triangles drawn with these dimensions will be congruent.

9. Abby wants her own cell phone. She and her parents have agreed that every month $10 will be taken from her savings to help pay for her service. Thanks to babysitting, she has $140 in her savings account.

a. Complete the table to show her balance, b, for each month, m.

$m =$	0	1	2	3	4	5	6
$b =$	140						

b. Write an equation for her balance, b, in terms of month, m. ____________________

c. How much money will be in her account after month 11? ____________________

10. a. Place -5 and -2 on the number line below.

b. True or false: -5 < -2 ? ________________

Lesson #15

Joke: Why did they put the mathematician in prison? He tried to kil-o-meter.

1. a. $10\frac{1}{6}$
$- 8\frac{1}{2}$

b. $3\frac{3}{4} \div 1\frac{2}{3} =$ ______

2. a. Draw a net for the square prism pictured at the right.

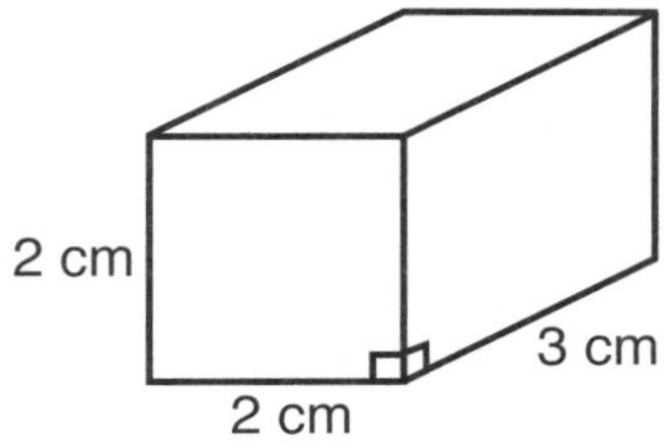

b. Find the surface area of the figure. ______________

c. The formula for the volume, V, of a prism with height, h, and base, B, is $V = Bh$. B is the area of the base. Find the volume of this prism.

____

3. $33\overline{)\$329.01}$

4. Two triangles are similar. The base of one is 2 inches and the height is 5 inches. If the base of the other is 7 inches, what is the height?

____

5. Simplify:

a. $2x + 4y - 2y + x$ ____________

b. $2x - 3(x + 4)$ ____________

6. a. Accurately draw ΔXYZ where $XY = 1.5$ inches, $YZ = 2$ inches, and $XZ = 3$ inches.

b. Explain why every triangle drawn with these dimensions will be congruent. ____________________

____

7. Choose the correct symbol (<, >, or =) for the following:

a. .248 __________ .25

b. $\frac{1}{3}$ __________ .3

c. -1.3 __________ -1.2

d. $\frac{4}{5}$ __________ $\frac{3}{4}$

8. Alec lives in New York City; his cousin Bonnie lives in Los Angeles, California. It is 3 hours earlier in Los Angeles than in New York City. Alec went to the show at 8:50 p.m. and returned $2\frac{1}{2}$ hours later. What time was it in "L.A." when Alec called Bonnie after the show?

____

9. Problem solving: If you weigh 60 pounds on earth, you would weigh 10 pounds on the moon. Calculate how much **you** would weigh on the moon (to the nearest pound.)

____

Lesson #16

1. a. $8\frac{1}{2} \div \frac{1}{\square} = 51$ b. $\frac{1}{2} \times \frac{1}{\square} = \frac{1}{8}$

2. Evaluate the following:

5 x 1 = ________   5 x 10 = ________   5 x 100 = ________   5 x 1,000 = ________

5 x 10,000 = ________   5 x 100,000 = ________   5 x 1,000,000 = ________

5 x 10,000,000 = ____________

Generalize: When $n > 0$, 5×10^n is __________ followed by ___________ zeros.

3. Help your friend Ima correct her mistake with this multiplication problem:

2.03 x .023 = 46.69

4. The Spanish club sold 250 boxes of candy for $3.50 each. The club is allowed to keep 30% of the money from each box sold. How much will the club make?

____

5. Mental math: Figure out this product by moving only the decimal.

.437628 x 10,000 = __________

Now check your answer on a calculator. Were you right?

6. Simplify:

a. $\frac{1^2 - 1^{10}}{1^{12}}$ = ________   b. $4 + 3(5-2)^2$ = ________   c. $4\left(\frac{3}{4}\right)^2$ = ________

Lesson #16 (continued)

7. a. Accurately draw ΔDEF where $\angle D = 40°$, $DE = 10$ cm, and $\angle E = 75°$.

b. Explain why all triangles drawn with these dimensions will be congruent.

____

____

8. For problems a and b, solve for x.

a. $-2x + 7 = -9$ ________

b. $\frac{1}{5}x = 4$ ________

9. Tao has $3\frac{3}{4}$ pounds of jelly beans. He wants to give each of his siblings $\frac{3}{4}$ pound and have an equal portion for himself. How many siblings does he have? __________

10. $\frac{5}{6} - \frac{1}{\square} = \frac{1}{2}$

Lesson #17

1. Mental math:

a. $12{,}000 \div 400 =$ ________ b. $4{,}000 + 3{,}000 + 200 =$ ________

2. a. $8\frac{5}{6} - 3\frac{1}{2}$ b. $5\frac{1}{8} - 2\frac{3}{4}$

3. Use cross products to show which of the properties are true. Circle all that are correct.

a. $\frac{2}{3} = \frac{66}{100}$ b. $\frac{4}{9} = \frac{8}{20}$ c. $\frac{4}{5} = \frac{44}{55}$

4. a. $2\frac{1}{10} \times 2\frac{3}{5} =$ ________ b. $\frac{2}{3} \div \frac{2}{5} =$ ________

5. What are the fewest number of coins needed to make 37% of a dollar?

____

6. Your baseball team scored 5 runs in the first 3 innings of a 9-inning game. If this rate continues, how many runs will be scored by the end of the game?

____

7. The earth is 93,000,000 miles from the sun. Write this number using scientific notation.

____

8. The number 15 can be written as the sum of consecutive numbers (numbers in a row). There are 3 ways.

a. _____ + _____ = 15

b. _____ + _____ + _____ = 15

c. _____ + _____ + _____ + _____ + _____ = 15

9. What is the greatest common factor for these numbers?

16, 20, 24 __________

10. Fill in the missing numbers in this equation: $\frac{6}{9} = \frac{\square}{27} = \frac{2}{\square} = \frac{24}{\square}$

11. The Fighting Irish won 7 games, lost 2 and tied 1. What percent of their games did they win?

____

12. Calculator skill: Find the sum of these two numbers: two thousand and seven tenths plus eighty-three hundredths.

____

Lesson #18

1. a. $21\overline{)1{,}984}$ b. $.009\overline{).081}$

2. Write each of the following as an algebraic expression. Let n = number.

a. Five less than a number plus 6 ____________________

b. Six more than a number squared ____________________

c. The opposite of a number plus -5 ____________________

3. Order from least to greatest:

$\frac{14}{15}$ $\frac{4}{5}$ $\frac{19}{20}$ $\frac{9}{10}$

__________ __________ __________ __________

4. A smoothie recipe uses $\frac{1}{4}$ cup of blueberries and $\frac{3}{4}$ cup of strawberries to make one smoothie.

a. Using whole numbers, what is the ratio of blueberries to strawberries? __________

b. You have 12 cups of strawberries; how many cups of blueberries do you need?

____

c. Assume you have enough strawberries. If you have $4\frac{1}{3}$ cups of blueberries, how many smoothies can you make?

____

5. A rectangular piece of cardboard is 8" x 10". Four 1" x 1" squares are cut from the corners and the sides are folded up to make a box. What is the volume of the box?

____

6. Given $\Delta ABC \cong \Delta XYZ$

From the given, mark each of the following true (T) or false (F).

a. $m\angle A = m\angle X$ __________ b. $BC = XY$ __________

c. $\overline{AB} \cong \overline{XY}$ __________ d. $\angle C \cong \angle Z$ __________

7. A *geometric sequence* is a number pattern where the ratio between consecutive terms is constant.

The first three terms of a geometric sequence are 64, 32, 16 ...

a. Find the next two terms. __________, __________

b. Find the ratio of two consecutive terms (next/previous). __________
This is the *common ratio*.

c. If the sixth term is 2, what is the seventh term? __________

8. Write in scientific notation:

a. 40 million ____________________ b. 3 trillion ____________________

9. Translate into a number sentence: *The sum of twice Billy's age, a, and 15 is 24.*

____

10. Everything in the store is discounted 15% for the next three hours. The bicycle you want is $159. You have $150. You know you will have a sales tax of 6%. Do you have enough money to buy the bicycle? Your work will justify your answer.

____

11. Find: $\sqrt{\dfrac{36}{49}}$

Lesson #19

1. a. $7 \div \frac{2}{3}$ = ____________ b. $2\frac{4}{5} \times \frac{1}{7}$ = ____________

2. The first three terms of a sequence are 6, 12, 24 …

a. Is this sequence arithmetic or geometric? ____________________

b. Find the next two terms. _________ , _________

3. Write as a decimal: $\frac{624}{10{,}000}$ ____________________

4. Solve each of the following for x. Some may have more than one answer.

a. $x^2 = 16$ ____________ b. $|x| = 8$ ____________ c. $\sqrt{x} = 5$ ____________

5. The forumla for distance, d, traveled at rate, r, for time, t, is $d = rt$.

a. You traveled for 4 hours at 65 mph. $d =$ ________________

b. You traveled 628 miles at 70 mph. $t =$ ________________

c. You traveled for x hours at 55 mph. $d =$ ________________

6. Paul's dinner cost $13.20. He wants to leave a 15% tip. How much money will he pay in all?

____

7. 3/5 of the earth is covered with water.

a. What fraction of the earth is land? __________ b. What % is land? __________

8. Evaluate each of the following:

a. $-8(5-3)^2 - 2 =$ __________ b. $\frac{4-2}{4} =$ __________

9. a. Find three pairs of points that satisfy the equation $x - y = 2$.

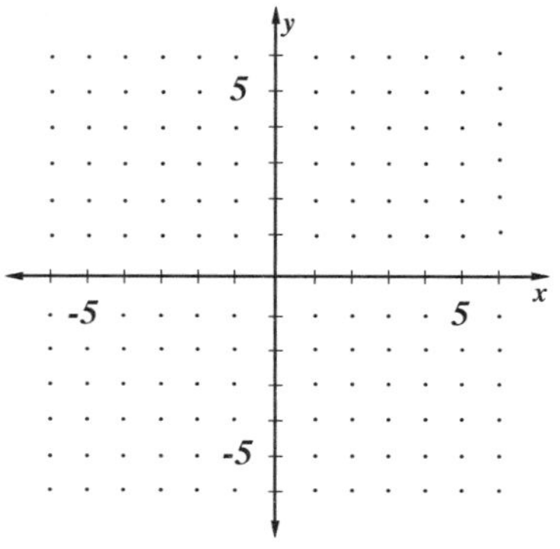

b. Plot the points on the coordinates at the right and draw a line through them.

c. Use two points and find the slope of the line.

10. Calculator skill: With a calculator find out how much the total order will cost using the menu below.

MENU	
Hamburgers	1.25
Cheeseburgers	1.35
French Fries	.65
Soft Drinks	.50

ORDER	
7	Hamburgers
8	Cheeseburgers
9	French Fries
15	Soft Drinks

____

Lesson #20

1. Use <, >, or = to make each sentence true.

a. (–2) (–2) (2) _____ (–2) (2) (2)

b. 1.0×10^4 _____ 1,000

c. $\frac{1}{4} \times \frac{1}{4}$ _____ $\frac{1}{4} \div \frac{1}{4}$

d. 10^2 _____ 2^{10}

2. Fahrenheit and Celsius temperatures are related by the following formula: $F = \frac{9}{5}C + 32$. One day in June the temperature in Cairo, Egypt reached 45 degrees Celsius. What is this in degrees Fahrenheit?

____

3. Rewrite using the *commutative property* (order) or the *associative property* (grouping), then solve mentally.

a. \$2.85 + \$4.50 + \$1.15 = ______________

b. $\frac{2}{5} + \frac{1}{3} + \frac{3}{5} + \frac{2}{3} =$ ______________

4. Tickets to the ball game are \$6.80 each. You have \$30. Estimate the number of tickets you can buy.

____

5. a. $\frac{1}{4} \times \frac{3}{5} =$ __________ b. $2\frac{1}{3} \div \frac{1}{6} =$ __________

6. Write this decimal in words: .0429

____

7. The first three terms of a *geometric sequence* are -4, 8, -16 ...

a. Find the next two terms. __________, __________

b. Find the common ratio. __________

c. Explain how to find each next term. ______________________________

8. What is another way to say 144? Circle all correct answers.

a. 12^2 b. 12^3 c. 12 x 12 d. 720 ÷ 5

9. What standard and metric units of measure could you use to determine how far you will run in a race?

____________________ ____________________

10. a. What is the numerical difference between one tenth and one one-hundredth?

____

b. What is the numerical difference between one one-hundredth and one one-thousandth?

____

11. Lena has a 50¢ off coupon for each of the 6 liters of soda pop she wants to buy. If each liter costs $1.59, how much will she pay for all 6 liters using her coupons?

____

12. Given $\Delta DEF \cong \Delta GHI$

From the given, mark each of the following true (T) or false (F).

a. perimeter (ΔDEF) = perimeter (ΔGHI) _____

b. $m\angle E = m\angle H$ _____ c. $\overline{DE} \cong \overline{HI}$ _____

Lesson #21

1. a. $$\begin{array}{r} 4\frac{1}{8} \\ -\ 3\frac{3}{4} \\ \hline \end{array}$$

b. $\frac{1}{2} + \frac{1}{4} + \frac{1}{8} =$ __________

2. Estimate by rounding each number to the nearest whole number:

$8.97 - 3.09 \approx$ ________________________

3. After a 20% markdown, the sale price of a pair of slacks is \$28.80. What was the original price? Let p = original price.

a. Write an equation to represent this situation. ______________________

b. Solve your equation. ______________________

4. Find three fractions equivalent to $\frac{2}{3}$ __________, __________, __________

5. a. $1\frac{3}{5} \div \frac{3}{5} =$ __________ b. $7\frac{1}{2} \times 3\frac{3}{5} =$ __________

6. Given a cube with: edge = 1 inch.

a. Find the volume of the cube. ___________

b. Double the size of the edge. Find the volume of the larger cube. ___________

c. The volume of the larger cube is __________ times that of the smaller.

7. Evaluate the following:

a. $-3 \times -7 =$ ________ b. $\left(-\frac{2}{3}\right)\left(-\frac{9}{10}\right) =$ ________ c. $-100 \times -40 =$ ________

d. Generalize: A negative times a negative is a ____________________.

8. Continue the pattern 1, 4, 9, 16, ________, ________, ________

9. Estimate the answer. 8,078 ÷ 97 = ___________

10. Use <, >, or = to compare.

a. $|4|$ ___________ $|-4|$ b. 4^2 ___________ $(-4)^2$

c. 2^4 ___________ 4^2 d. 4^1 ___________ 4×10^0

11. In the Florida Everglades, the number of wading birds (such as egrets and herons) has decreased by 90% in the past 75 years. At one time there were 300,000 wading birds. How many are there now?

____

12. Calculator skill: Enter on a calculator: 81,116 + 7,293 + 10,201 + 3,017. Do not press =. Circle your choice for the best estimate of the sum.

a. 110,000 b. 101,000 c. 100,000

Now press = to see if your choice was correct.

Lesson #22

1. a. $18\frac{1}{3} - 7\frac{5}{6}$

b. $14\frac{1}{10} - 2\frac{3}{4}$

2. a. 12 out of 100 is __________%

b. 12 out of 50 is __________%

c. 12 out of 25 is __________%

3. Order these improper fractions from least to greatest:

$\frac{47}{5}$ $\frac{56}{6}$ $\frac{64}{7}$ $\frac{78}{8}$

a. __________ b. __________ c. __________ d. __________

4. Mental math: Every second 2,000,000 red blood cells are manufactured by the human body. How many are manufactured in one minute?

____

5. $72\overline{)394}$

6. Complete this table:

$1^3 =$ ______ $2^3 =$ ______ $3^3 =$ ______ $4^3 =$ ______ $5^3 =$ ______

Lesson #22 (continued)

7. Find the value of n: $\frac{64}{8}n = 24$ n = ________

8. Circle the factors of 72: 6 9 4 7 3 8 5 2

9. Find the area of a triangle with a base of 6 inches and a height of 8 inches.

Area = ________

10. a. $\frac{2}{5} \times \frac{3}{10} =$ ________ b. $5\frac{2}{3} \div 2\frac{1}{4} =$ ________

11. If the probability is that the number 8 will be chosen in a drawing two out of every six times, how many times would you expect the number eight to be chosen out of eighteen drawings?

____

12. A *rate* is a quotient of two numbers in different units. Mr. Vonk, the principal, will shave his head if his students read 2,500 books during the month of February. There are 720 students in the school.

a. Write this rate in terms of books per student (Round the number of books to the nearest tenth.)

____

b. At the end of the month, each student read an average of 3 books. Did Mr. Vonk need to shave his head?

____

Lesson #23

1. a. $6\frac{3}{4} \div 3\frac{3}{4} =$ __________ b. $1\frac{3}{5} \div 5 =$ __________

2. Estimate by rounding to the nearest whole number:

a. $5.11 \times 6.98 \approx$ __________ b. $4.9 - 5.3 + 7.2 \approx$ __________

3. a. Draw the net for the cylinder pictured to the right.

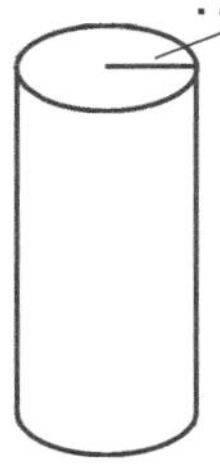

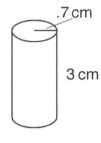

b. Find the surface area. Use $\pi = 3.14$ and round to the nearest tenth.

____

c. Find the volume. Round to the nearest tenth. __________

4. Mental math: Humans dream about 20% of the time they are asleep. If you sleep ten hours per night, how much time will you be dreaming?

____

5. $4.8\overline{)478.56}$

6. In a golf tournament, Sol was 2 strokes over par the first day, 5 strokes over par the second day, even par the third day and 3 strokes under par the fourth day. How many strokes was Sol under or over par for the tournament?

____

7. Mental math: Find each product.

a. $200 \times 30 =$ ________ b. $500 \times 1{,}000 =$ ________

c. $300 \times 600 =$ ________ d. $100 \times 1{,}000{,}000 =$ ________

8. Mental math: $4{,}700 - 699 =$ ________

9. a. 468 inches = ________ feet = ________ yards

b. 59,000 mm = ________ cm = ________ m

10. Mental math:

a. $\frac{3}{10} \times \frac{1}{2} =$ ________ b. $10 \div \frac{1}{5} =$ ________

11. The appearance of a graph can influence how you interpret the results. Each middle school in a certain district has graphic calculators in the classroom for student use. Use the graph pictured below to answer the questions.

a. What does the graph suggest about the number of graphic calculators at Central Middle versus Eastern Middle?

____

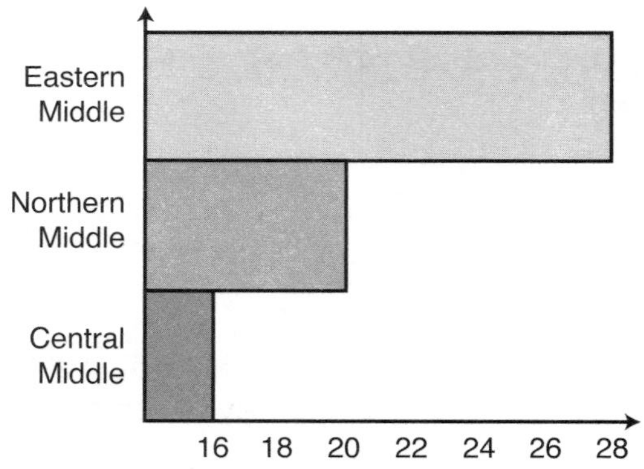

b. Use a separate sheet of paper to redraw the graph without the break. Which school might find the redrawn graph more favorable?

____

Lesson #24

1. a. $\frac{1}{3} \times 4\frac{1}{5} =$ __________ b. $\frac{1}{4} \times \frac{3}{8} =$ __________

2. Circle which fraction is between 1/3 and 1/2.

a. $\frac{3}{9}$ b. $\frac{4}{9}$ c. $\frac{6}{9}$

3. What is the appropriate unit of measure?

__________	height of a basketball player	a. millimeters
__________	distance from Chicago to Detroit	b. meters
__________	diameter of a dime	c. centimeters
__________	diagonal of a computer screen	d. kilometers

4. Find the value of n. $2 + n + n = 8$ n = __________

5. a. Draw and label all the rectangles with integer dimensions that have an area of 12 square feet.

b. Find the perimeter of each rectangle.

c. If fencing costs $3.00 a foot, which rectangle is the least expensive? __________

6. Mental math: Find each quotient.

a. 600 ÷ 10 = ______ b. 9,000 ÷ 30 = ______ c. 1,000,000 ÷ 100 = ______

Lesson #24 (continued)

7. Brie has 3 pairs of shorts, 6 shirts, and 2 sweaters. How many different outfits can she create?

____

8. One milliliter of water weighs one gram. What is the weight, in grams, of a liter of water?

____

9. Let $x = -2$. Find each of the following:

a. $|x|$ __________ b. x^2 __________ c. $(-x)^2$ __________

10. In many cities, a realtor receives a commission of 5.5% of the selling price of a home. A certain home sold for $1,800,000. What was the commission?

____

11. The temperature before the sled race began was -7˚F. When the race was over, it was 11˚F. How many degrees did the temperature rise?

____

12. Circle which of the following is not equivalent to the others:

a. .35 b. $\frac{1}{3}$ c. $\frac{70}{200}$ d. .350

Lesson #25

1. The baseball team won 3/4 of its first 20 games. How many games must the team win in its next 12 games to keep its average the same?

____

2. For problems a – c, solve for x.

a. $3x + 6 = -9$ ________ b. $\frac{2}{3}x = \frac{5}{9}$ ________ c. $-2x = -5$ ________

3. Circle the better estimate for the volume of a salt shaker.

a. 46 liters b. 46 milliliters

4. Figure A contains even numbers. Figure B contains the numbers 1, 5, 7, 8, 11, 20. What are points Y and Z?

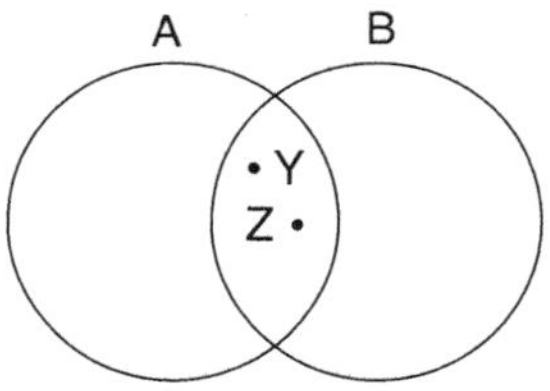

____

5. Nihal scored 65, 79, 92, 100, and 100 on his math tests.

a. Find his mean score. ________________

b. Find his median score. ________________

c. If 85 – 88 is a B+ grade and 89 – 92 is an A-, what grade would you give him?

____

6. a. Friday you are driving to a city 312 miles away. You average 60 mph. Estimate the amount of time for this trip.

____

b. Your car averages about 30 miles per gallon of gas. Estimate the number of gallons of gas you will need.

____

7. Estimate the difference by rounding: 7,012 − 198 = __________

8. Mental math:

a. 540 ÷ 60 = __________

b. 725 + 5,050 + 325 = __________

c. 80 x 90 = __________

9.

a.
$$\begin{array}{r} 9.45 \\ \times\ \ 3.2 \\ \hline \end{array}$$

b.
$$\begin{array}{r} .083 \\ \times\ \ .02 \\ \hline \end{array}$$

10. If you want to leave a 15% tip, how much should you leave for a $45.00 meal?

____

11. Natasha read the following story problem: "If you saved 1/20 of your paycheck each week, how much money would you save in ten weeks?" She realized that part of the story problem was missing. What part was missing?

____

12. Fill in the missing numbers in this sequence.

52 45 38 _____ 24 _____ 10 _____

Lesson #26

1. Complete the chart:

Percent	Fraction	Decimal
20		
	$\frac{1}{10}$	
80		
		$.33\overline{3}$

2. Simplify the following polynomials:

a. $3x^2 - x + 2x^2 - x$ ______________ b. $4x^2 - 5(x^2 - x)$ ______________

3. The sum of two integers is 20. The difference between the two numbers is 8. What are the two numbers? (Hint: Write the possible sums, then check their differences.)

________ ________

4. Write the following sentence in algebraic notation: *Three more than five times a number is 15.*

____

5. On a recent trip the Millers drove 392 miles and used 14 gallons of gasoline. How many miles per gallon did they average?

____

6. Batting averages are found by dividing hits by times at bat. They are expressed as decimals to the nearest thousandth. John is an amazing hitter. In his first 150 times at bat he has hit successfully 73 times. What is his batting average?

____

7. Evaluate each of the following:

a. $\sqrt{9} =$ ______ b. $\sqrt{49} =$ ______ c. $\sqrt{\frac{1}{36}} =$ ______ d. $\sqrt{.01} =$ ______

Lesson #26 (continued)

8. a. Find three pairs of numbers that satisfy $x + y = 4$.

b. Graph this line on the coordinates at the right.

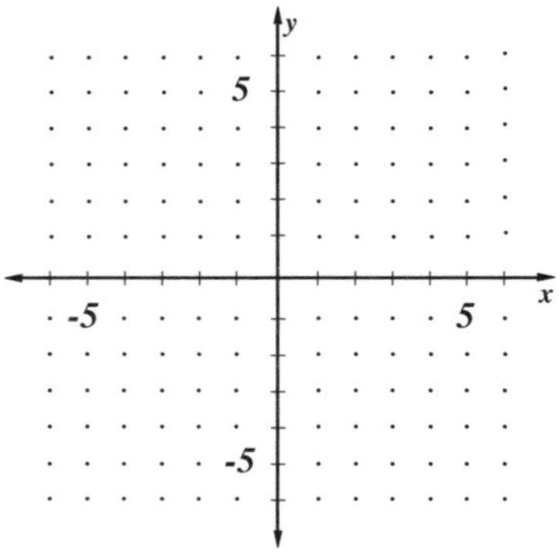

c. Find three pairs of numbers that satisfy $y = 3x$. ______________

d. Graph this line on the same coordinates.

e. The two lines intersect at what point? __________
This is the *solution set* for this system.

9. Order from smallest to largest.

$\sqrt{\frac{9}{25}}$ $\frac{2}{3}$ 62% .66

_________ _________ _________ _________

10. The ages and weights of three people were graphed.

a. Who weighs the most? _________

b. Who is the oldest? __________

c. Who is the youngest? __________

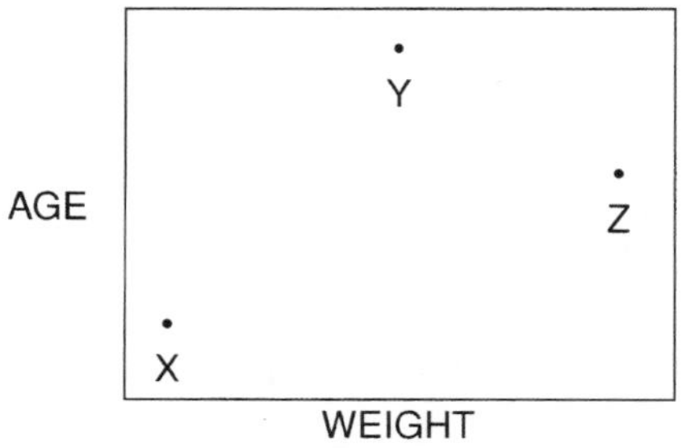

11. Find 120% of 100. __________

Lesson #27

1. Circle the best estimate for the length of a car:

a. 5.5 millimeters b. 5.5 centimeters c. 5.5 meters

2. a. 10.04 – .684 = __________ b. 5.4 – .003 =__________

3. Mental math:

a. 3,768 ÷ 100 = __________ b. 74.99 ÷ 100 = __________

c. .2 ÷ 100 = __________ d. 560,000 ÷ 100 = __________

4. Write 4 numbers that meet all the requirements listed below.

a. not more than 50 b. more than 12
c. divisible by 8 d. not divisible by 10

__________ __________ __________ __________

5. a. Given $y = x^2$. Complete the table below.

$x =$	–2	–1	0	1	2
$y =$					

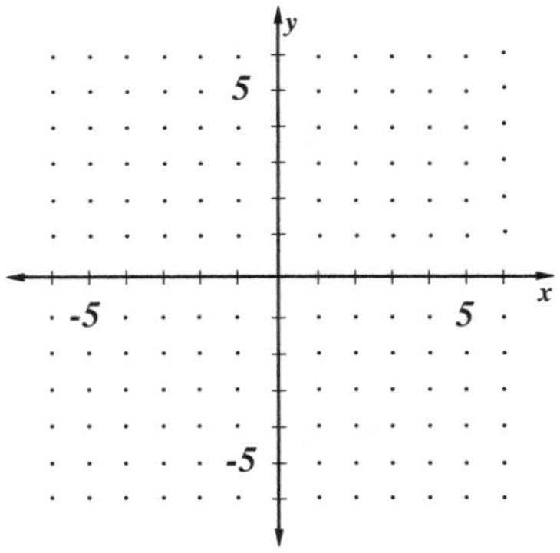

b. Plot these points on the coordinates at the right. Notice your graph is not a line. This graph is a *parabola*.

6. Ken makes picture frames. Each frame requires $6\frac{1}{4}$ feet of wood. If he has 60 feet of wood, how many frames can he make?

____

7. A parking lot for a strip mall must be $\frac{3}{8}$ square mile. The length is $\frac{3}{4}$ mile. What is the width?

____

8. The area of a square is $\frac{1}{9}$ of a square foot.

a. What is the length of one side? _______________

b. What is the perimeter? _______________

9. a. $4 - 3\frac{5}{6} =$ __________ b. $3\frac{5}{12} + 5\frac{7}{12} =$ __________

10. Express as a percent:

a. $\frac{1}{100} =$ __________% b. .001 = __________%

11. In a deck of 52 cards there are 13 spades, 13 hearts, 13 diamonds, and 13 clubs. You select one card from the deck.

a. What is the probability of drawing a spade? _______________

b. What is the probability of drawing the jack of hearts? _______________

c. What is the probability of drawing a card that is either a club or a diamond?

____

12. Calculator skill: In 1969 Neil Armstrong journeyed to the moon in his spaceship, Apollo XI. He traveled at a speed of .6912789 miles per second. How far did he travel in 1 hour?

____

Lesson #28

1. a. $4\frac{1}{2} \times 4\frac{1}{4} =$ ________ b. $\frac{15}{16} \div 1\frac{7}{8} =$ ________

2. Mental math:

a. 15 ÷ .03 = ______________ b. .15 ÷ .03 = ______________

3. Which is the best estimate for the weight of a dishwasher?

a. 37 grams b. 37 kilograms

4. In July 2011, the population of the United States was estimated to be 313,000,000. Write this number in scientific notation.

____

5. Children three and under are free.

a. Write this as an inequality. Remember, there are no negative ages.

____

b. Graph this on the line below.

```
----------|----------|----------|----------|----------|----------|----------|----------
         -1          0          1          2          3          4          5
```

6. Stahl's Boutique marks coats up 50%.

a. What is the price of a $90 coat before the mark up? ________

b. If the sales person at Stahl's makes a 3% commission, how much would the commission be for the $90 coat?

____

7. Mental math:

a. 4,000 x 300 = ____________   b. 72,000,000 ÷ 9,000 = ____________

8. Find the least common multiple of 2, 4, 6. ____________________

9. Solve for x. (Hint: use the property of reciprocals.)

a. $\frac{3}{7}x = \frac{15}{22}$ ______   b. $\frac{5}{9}x = 60$ ______   c. $-\frac{3}{11}x = \frac{3}{44}$ ______

10. Continue the pattern:

100, 2, 95, 4, 90, 6, 85, 8, _____, _____, _____, _____

11. Melinda has $4\frac{1}{2}$ yards of ribbon left on a spool. She is making hair bows for her friends. Each requires $\frac{3}{8}$ yard.

a. How many can she make? ______________

b. How much ribbon will she have left over? ________________

12. The dimensions of a room are 12' x 14'.

a. Find the area of this room. ________________

b. Carpet is sold by the square yard. How much carpet will you need to cover the floor? (1 sq. yard = 9 square feet) Round to the nearest whole yard.

____

Lesson #29

1. a. $3\frac{1}{2} + 2\frac{1}{8} =$ ________ b. $6\frac{1}{8} - 2\frac{3}{4} =$ ________

2. Mental math: Use the commutative property to find:

2 x 29 x 50 = ______________

3. Find the mean of the bowling scores below. __________

101 128 98 156 130

4. Estimate:

a. 30,157 ÷ 29 ___________ b. 4,189 x 512 ___________

5. a. $8 - 2\frac{3}{10} =$ __________ b. $2\frac{3}{4} + 1\frac{1}{2} =$ __________

6. The sum of two angles is 90°. The larger is twice the smaller.
Let a = smaller angle.

a. Write a math sentence to represent this situation.

____

b. Find the measure of both angles. __________

7. What is the greatest common factor for these numbers? 63, 54, 81

____

8. Mental math:

a. 28,050 + 3,050 = __________ b. 5,420 – 4,421 = __________

9. a. $3\frac{1}{6} \times 1\frac{1}{10} =$ __________ b. $\frac{1}{2} \div 1\frac{1}{4} =$ __________

10. Write these percents as decimals:

a. 18.5% __________ b. 200% __________ c. .5% __________

11. The first week of school Kim studied 11 hours and 25 minutes. The second week he studied 9 hours and 45 minutes, and the third week 10 hours and 58 minutes. How much time did he study during these 3 weeks?

____

12. A die with 6 faces is tossed. The faces are numbered from 1 – 6. Find the probability of each of the following:

a. Probability of tossing a 6 ____________________

b. Probability of tossing an even number ____________________

c. Probability of tossing a number greater than 5 ____________________

Lesson #30

1. Solve for x.

a. $8x - 2 = -10$ ________ b. $\frac{3}{4}x = 15$ ________ c. $1.2x = .36$ ________

2.

$$\begin{array}{r} 7\frac{3}{8} \\ +\ 13\frac{3}{16} \\ \hline \end{array}$$

3. A certain room is 10' x 12'.

a. Find the area of the room.

____

b. A floor is to be tiled with square tiles 18 inches on a side. How many are needed to complete the job? Round up to the nearest whole tile.

____

4. $1\frac{1}{2}$ pounds of chicken cost $4.50. What is the price per pound? __________

5. a. Counting by <u>thousandths</u>, what comes after 9.709? __________

b. Counting by <u>ten thousandths</u>, what comes after 9.709? __________

6. The diameter of the earth is 12,756.2 kilometers. Write this number in scientific notation.

____

7. The items in your grocery cart cost the following:

$4.95 $.99 $1.19 $6.79 $3.80

Estimate: If you have $20, do you have enough to cover your purchases?

____

8. Solve for x. Some may have more than one answer.

a. $x^2 = 16$ ______ b. $|x| = 4$ ______ c. $\sqrt{x} = 2$ ______

9. Use <, >, or = to make each sentence true.

a. $6 \times 3 \div 2$ _________ $6 \div 3 \times 2$ b. $\left(\frac{1}{2}\right)^3$ _________ $\left(\frac{1}{3}\right)^2$

c. 1.0^4 _________ $1{,}000^0$ d. $(-2)^3$ _________ 2^3

10. a. -6.7 is between what two integers? __________ and __________

b. Round -6.7 to the nearest integer. _______________

11. Which of the choices below would best describe the following sentence?
Most of the people in Jan's class like chocolate ice cream the best.

a. 2/5 of the people liked chocolate best.
b. 5/5 of the people liked chocolate best.
c. 4/5 of the people liked chocolate best.

____

12. Mental math: What number am I? I am between 1-50. I am divisible by 7. I am an even number. My ten's place digit has twice the value of my one's place digit.

____

1. For problems, a – c, simplify. (Recall that the order of operations is: parentheses, powers, multiplication and division from left to right; addition and subtraction from left to right.)

a. $(2-4)^2 / 1 + 1$ b. $8 - 8 / 2 \times 2$ c. $\dfrac{7-1^2}{4-2}$

2. A *variable* is a symbol that can be replaced by a number.

Let $a = -2$ $b = -\frac{1}{2}$ $c = \frac{1}{2}$ $d = 2$ Find the following:

a. ab b. a^2 c. $-b^2$

d. $\dfrac{b}{d}$ e. $-a + d$ f. $abcd$

3. *Expressions* occur when numbers and variables are joined using arithmetic operations. Translate the following into algebraic expressions. Let n =number.

a. Five more than twice a number ____________________

b. Six less than half of a number ____________________

c. A number squared plus two ____________________

d. The opposite of a number ____________________

4. A *polynomial* is an expression written as the sum or difference of terms. To simplify a polynomial, combine *like* terms. Simplify the following:

a. $2a + 3b - 6a + b$ b. $4x^2 - x - 3x^2 + x$

5. The mean, median, and mode are measures of *central tendency.* Find the mean, median, and mode for the given number set.

2 2 3 0 2 9 8 8 4 2 3 25 80

a. mean __________ b. median __________ c. mode __________

d. Which is the best representation of middle or central tendency? Justify.

6. A *ratio* is the quotient of two quantities in the same unit.

The ski club has 12 girls and 7 boys.

a. Find the ratio of girls to boys.

b. Find the ratio of girls to the club membership.

7. For problems a – c, solve for x.

a. $3x + 5 = -4$ b. $\frac{2}{3}x = 6$ c. $-x + 8 = -4$

8. Use the *distributive* property to find the missing number or variable.

a. $4(x - y) = 4(\quad) - 4(\quad)$ b. $8a - 16b = (\quad)(a - 2b)$

9. a. Find three pairs of points that satisfy the equation $x + y = 3$.

b. Plot the points on the graph at the right and draw a line through them.

c. The slope or constant rate of change of a linear equation is the ratio of the rise/run. Pick a point on the line and then, reading the graph from left to right, find the rise and run to get to another point on the graph.

d. Substitute your point into the equation to verify that it is on the line.

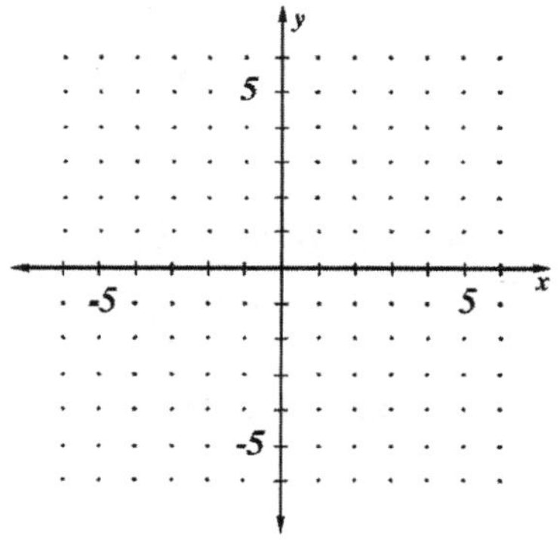

10. Write each number using scientific notation.

a. 43200 _______________ b. 1,000,000 _______________

c. .00502 _______________ d. 5 _______________

1. **Use <, >, *or* = to make each sentence true.**

a. $4 \times 6 \div 3$ _____ $6 \div 3 \times 4$

b. $\left(\frac{1}{2}\right)^3$ _____ $\left(\frac{1}{3}\right)^2$

c. $\frac{1}{4} \times \frac{1}{4}$ _____ $\frac{1}{4} \div \frac{1}{4}$

d. 1.0^6 _____ $1{,}000{,}000^0$

e. $4 - (4 \div 4) \times 4$ _____ $(4 - 4) \div 4 \times 4$

f. $2 \times 3 + 4$ _____ $2 + 3 \times 4$

2. **A *rational number* is one that can be written as the ratio of two integers. *Integers* are whole numbers and their opposites.**

Show that each number below is rational by renaming it as a fraction.

a. 4 b. −8 c. .9 d. .125

e. 25% f. $.\overline{3}$ g. .3 h. 6.5%

3. **A *number sentence* is formed when two expressions are related using a math verb. Examples of math verbs are: <, >, =, ≤, ≥, ≠. When two expressions are equal, the sentence is an equation. Translate each of the following into a number sentence:**

   a. Rate multiplied by time is distance. _______________

   b. \$.10 times *n* cans returned is \$5.50. _______________

   c. Anna is *a* years old. Katie is 7 years old. Katie's age is more than twice Anna's. _______________

   d. Ten is less than three times the number. _______________

4. **The *absolute value* of a number is its positive distance from zero. Find the absolute value of the following:**

a. $|-8|$ b. $|4-8|$ c. $|4|+|-8|$

5. **Simplify:**

a. $3a - b - 3a$ b. $2(x + y) - 2x + 2y$ c. $2(4x)^2$

6. An *arithmetic sequence* is a number pattern where the difference between consecutive numbers (terms) is constant.

The first three terms of a sequence are 2, 6, 10, ...

a. Find the next two terms in the sequence. _____, _____

b. Find the difference between consecutive terms. (next term – previous term) _____. This is the constant difference or constant rate of change.

c. Find a rule for any term in the sequence.

d. Use your rule to find the tenth term. _______________

7. When two rates or ratios are equal, they are *proportional.* Which of the following proportions are true? (Hint: Use cross products.)

a. $\frac{2}{3} = \frac{21}{33}$ b. $\frac{5}{6} = \frac{83}{100}$ c. $\frac{4}{5} = \frac{16}{20}$

8. A *formula* is an equation stating that a single variable is equal to an expression. The circumference (c) of a circle with radius (r) is $c = 2\pi r$. Let $r = 2$ inches.

a. Find the exact circumference of the circle.

b. Approximate the circumference to the nearest tenth. (Use $\pi \approx 3.14$.)

9. Choose from the associative property, commutative property, or distributive property to justify each of the following:

a. $6 + 42 - 6 + 8 = 6 - 6 + 42 + 8 = 50$ _______________

b. $4x + 8y = 4(x + 2y)$ _______________

c. $(50 \times 9) \times (8 \times 2) = (50 \times 2) \times (9 \times 8) = 100 \times 72 = 7200$ _______________

10. Let $x = -2$. Find the following:

a. $x^2 - x$ b. $x^3 + x^2 + x$ c. $|x|$

1. For problems, a – c, simplify.

a. $(6+2)^2 / 16 \times 4$ b. $8 - 2^3 / 2$ c. $\frac{8-2^3}{2}$

2. The formula for finding the rate of change or slope m between two points (x_1, y_1) and (x_2, y_2) is $m = \frac{y_2 - y_1}{x_2 - x_1}$. Find the slope between $(0, 4)$ and $(2, -8)$.

3. An *irrational* number is one that cannot be written as a ratio of two integers. Write R next to each rational number and I next to each irrational number.

a. 25% b. $\sqrt{2}$ c. $\sqrt{\frac{1}{4}}$ d. π e. $\frac{22}{7}$

4. Henry has scores of 81, 85, 87, 92, and 98 on his first five math tests.

a. Find his mean score.

b. What must he score on his next test to have an average of 90?

5. Match each area formula with its geometric figure.

a. $A = lw$ __________ trapezoid

b. $A = \pi r^2$ __________ square

c. $A = bh$ __________ rectangle

d. $A = \frac{1}{2}hb$ __________ circle

e. $A = \frac{1}{2}h(b_1 + b_2)$ __________ triangle

f. $A = s^2$ __________ parallelogram

6. If two angles are *supplementary,* then the sum of the two angles is 180°.

   The measure of one angle is three times the measure of another.

   a. Write a math sentence to represent this situation.

   b. Find the measure of each angle.

7. Suppose $a > 1$, $0 < b < 1$, $c < -1$, $-1 < d < 0$. Use <, >, or = to make each statement true.

   a. a^{-1} _____ b^{-1} b. b^2 _____ d^2

   c. a^0 _____ c^0 d. b _____ b^2

   e. $-a^2$ _____ $(-a)^2$ f. $a + c$ _____ $b + d$

8. A bag contains marbles in three different colors. Eight are blue, five are green, and two are red. A marble is drawn at random. Find the following:

   a. $P\ (green) =$ b. $P(blue\ or\ red) =$

   c. $P(not\ \ blue) =$ d. $P(black) =$

   e. Two marbles are drawn. Find *P(first red and second green)* =

9. Given ΔABC with $A = (-3, 2)$ $B = (-1, 2)$ $C = (-1, -1)$

   a. Graph ΔABC on the coordinates at the right.

   b. A translation T is defined by a horizontal move of h units and a vertical move of k units. The notation is $T_{h\ \ k}(image)$.

   Find and graph $T_{2\ \ -1}(\Delta ABC) = \Delta A'B'C'$

   c. A reflection r is defined as a transformation in which each point is mapped onto its reflection image over a line. The notation is $r_{line}(image)$.

   Find and graph $r_{y-axis}(\Delta ABC) = \Delta A''B''C''$

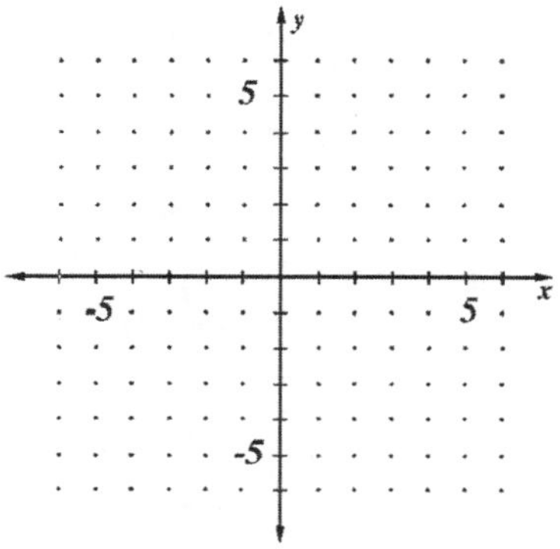

1. **For problems, a – c, solve for x.**

   a. $x^2 = 25$ b. $|x| = 2$ c. $2^x = 16$

2. a. **Accurately draw a square with side $(s) = 1$".**

   b. **Accurately draw a square with $s = 3$".**

   c. **Find the perimeter of each square.**

   d. **Find the area of each square.**

   e. **The perimeter of the larger square is _____ times the perimeter of the smaller square.**

   f. **The area of the larger square is _____ times the area of the smaller square.**

3. **Use the figure pictured at the right. Find the measure of each of the following:**

   a. $m\angle 1 =$ b. $m\angle 2 =$

   c. $m\angle 3 =$ d. $m\angle 4 =$

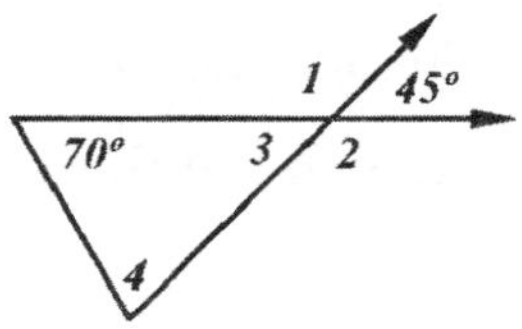

4. a. **Find the area of a trapezoid with $h = 4$", $b_1 = 6$", $b_2 = 8$".**

   b. **Another trapezoid has an area of 32 inches^2, $h = 4$", and the bases of equal length. Find the lengths of the bases.**

5. **The *Pythagorean theorem* states that in a right triangle, the square of the hypotenuse is equal to the sum of the squares of the other two sides (called legs). $c^2 = a^2 + b^2$. Given $a = 5$, $b = 12$, find c.**

6. How many hours a week do you spend watching television? The students in your math class gave the following responses:

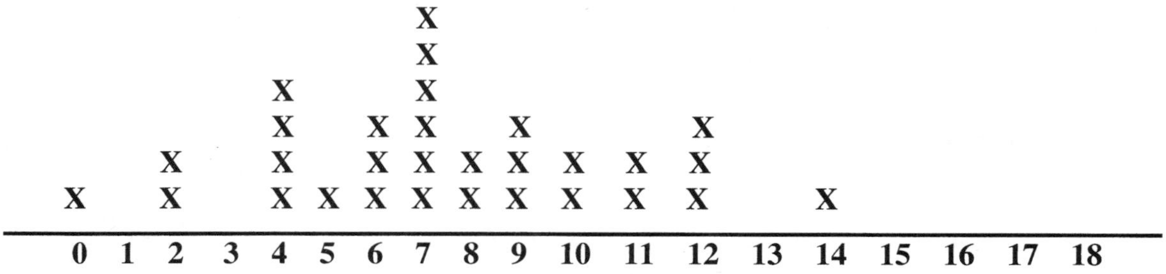

a. **What is the upper extreme? __________**

b. **What is the lower extreme? __________**

c. **What is the median? __________**

d. **What is the upper quartile? __________**

e. **What is the lower quartile? __________**

f. **What is the inter quartile range (IQR)? This is the upper quartile minus the lower quartile. __________**

7. The product of two numbers is -20. The sum of the two numbers is -8. Find the two numbers.

8. The area of a circular garden is 85 square feet. To the nearest tenth, find the diameter.

9. Solve these proportions for x:

a. $\frac{x}{6} = \frac{3}{8}$ b. $\frac{x}{15} = \frac{5}{75}$ c. $\frac{x^2}{4} = \frac{9}{25}$

1. A perfectly square lot has a perimeter of exactly one mile.
   a. Find the length of one side.
   b. Find the area of the lot.

2. Consider the polynomial $4x^5 - 3x^3 - 2x + 1$.
   a. How many terms are in this expression? __________
   b. What is the coefficient of x^3? __________
   c. What is the degree of this polynomial? __________
   d. What is the constant? __________

3. A biased sample is one in which members of a population are underrepresented or ignored totally.

   Should students be allowed to chew gum during class?

   The audience at a choir concert was surveyed and the majority of those in attendance said "no."

   Explain why this sample might be biased.

4. A family has four children. Find each probability. The order does not matter. (Hint, make a tree diagram.)
   a. $P(4\ boys)$
   b. $P(2\ boys\ and\ 2\ girls)$
   c. $P(3\ boys\ and\ 1\ girl)$

5. Verify that 1, 2, and $\sqrt{5}$ are lengths of the sides of a right triangle.

6. Do the following problems mentally by rearranging (commutative) or regrouping (associative) the numbers.
   a. \$2.30 + \$4.95 + \$1.70
   b. $-5 + 9 + 5 + 1$
   c. $\frac{1}{3}(17)(3)$
   d. $\frac{1}{3} + \frac{1}{5} + \frac{2}{3} + \frac{4}{5}$

7. Evaluate:

a. $\frac{1}{3}(3) =$ b. $\left(\frac{2}{5}\right)\left(\frac{5}{2}\right) =$ c. $.1(10) =$

d. Generalize: $\frac{1}{n} \bullet n =$ $n \neq 0$

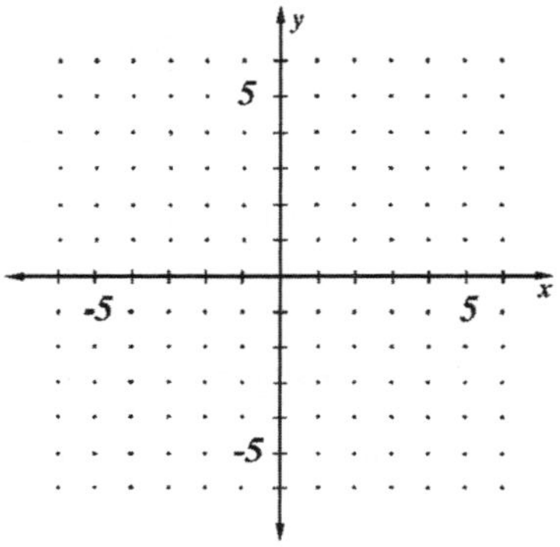

8. a. Find three ordered pairs that satisfy the equation $x - y = 4$.

b. Plot the points on the graph at the right and draw a line through them.

c. Select two points and find the slope of this line.

9. Given point $P = (2, 1)$, find:

a. $T_{-2\ -1}(P) =$ b. $r_{x-axis}(P) =$ c. $r_{y-axis}(P) =$

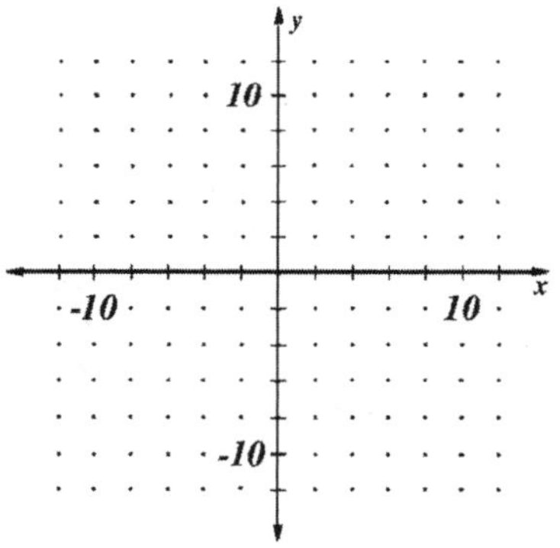

10. a. Complete the table for $y = x^2$

$x =$	-3	-2	-1	0	1	2	3
$y =$							

b. Plot the points on the coordinates at the right and connect them with a smooth curve.

c. Identify the figure.

11. How many ways can the four members of Harper's bowling team line up for a picture?

12. a. Write the following sentence in algebraic notation: *Three times a number and its opposite is –8.*

b. Find the number.

BRAIN AEROBICS - WEEK 1

1. What is the sum of all the prime numbers between 10 and 20?

2. Judith is 5 years younger than Trina and 5 years older than Gretchen. The average of their ages is 23. How old is each woman?

3. Pamela can swim under water for 51 seconds without a breath. Lucy can swim $\frac{3}{5}$ minute and Kady .8 minute. Who can stay underwater the longest?

4. Mr. Jackson spends $500 per month for rent. His new apartment will cost him 10% more than he is paying now. How much is the rent for his new apartment?

5. Find the set of counting numbers which would make this equation true.

$20 - x \rangle 14$

Solutions – Brain Aerobics – Week 1 – 7th Grade

1. $11 + 13 + 17 + 19 = 60$

2. Judith = x years old
Trina = x + 5 years old
Gretchen = x - 5 years old

$$\frac{x + (x + 5) + (x - 5)}{3} = 23$$

$$\frac{3x}{3} = 23$$

$$x = 23$$

Judith is 23.
Trina is 28.
Gretchen is 18.

3. Pamela = 51 seconds
Lucy = $\frac{3}{5} \times 60 = \frac{180}{5} = 36$ seconds
Kady = $.8 \times 60 = 48$ seconds

Pamela can stay underwater the longest.

4. $500 \times .10 = 50$
$500 + 50 = \$550.00$

5.

$$\begin{aligned} 20 - x &> 14 \\ -20 \quad & \quad -20 \\ -x &> -6 \\ x &< 6 \end{aligned}$$

BRAIN AEROBICS - WEEK 2

1. Ana weighed 8 pounds at birth. By age 2 months, her weight had increased by 60%. How much did she weigh at 2 months?

2. Soren earned money by shoveling snow for his neighbors. Mr. Rodriguez paid him $1.00 for every 10 minutes of work. Mrs. Kaylor paid him $2.00 for every .4 hour. Which neighbor paid him the most money per hour?

3. Bonnie bought 2 pounds of hamburger meat. She made each of her two older children a $\frac{1}{4}$ pound hamburger and each of her 3 younger children a 3 ounce hamburger. How much hamburger meat did Bonnie have left after all of her children were served?

4. Katarina's job at the zoo is feeding Elmo and Elvira, the elephants. The elephants weigh a total of 7 tons. Katarina weighs 1% of that combined weight. How much does Katarina weigh?

5. Cassie ordered $1\frac{1}{2}$ gallons of ice cream for her birthday party. She had one quart of mint chip ice cream. Write the fraction that shows the ratio of the mint chip ice cream to the total amount.

Solutions – Brain Aerobics – Week 2 – 7th Grade

1. 60% = .60
8 x .60 + 4.8
8 + 4.8 = 12.8 pounds

2. 1 hour = 60 minutes
60 ÷ 10 = 6
$1.00 x 6 = $6.00 per hour from Mr. Rodriguez
1 ÷ .4 = 2.5
$2.00 x 2.5 = $5.00 per hour from Mr. Kaylor
Mr. Rodriguez paid more per hour.

3. 1 pound = 16 ounces   2 x 16 = 32 ounces of meat
16 x .25 = 4 ounces
4 x 2 = 8 ounces for the 2 older children
3 x 3 = 9 ounces for the 3 younger children
8 + 9 = 17 ounces used
32 – 17 = 15 ounces left

4. 1 ton = 2,000 pounds
7 x 2,000 = 14,000 pounds
14,000 x .01 = 140 pounds

5. 4 quarts = 1 gallon
4 x 1.5 = 6 quarts
$\frac{1}{6}$ of the ice cream was mint chip

BRAIN AEROBICS - WEEK 3

1. The five players on the basketball team scored an average of 18 points each. Charles scored 27 points. Three of the other players scored 15 points, 15 points, and 16 points respectively. How many points did the 5th player score?

2. What number am I? I am divisible by 2 and 3. I am greater than 40 and less than 60. When you divide my first digit by my second digit, you get 2.

3. Travis was asked to choose the winning ticket in a raffle. Three hundred tickets were sold by the girls' basketball team, 200 tickets by the girls' field hockey team, and 100 tickets by the girls' soccer team. What is the probability that a ticket sold by the soccer team will be drawn?

4. Pia saw the same backpack at 2 different stores. The first backpack sells for $49 with a $5 rebate. The second backpack is on sale for 30% off the original $60 price. Which one is the better value?

5, Seth spent 3 hours at the park. He ran for 20 minutes. Write the fraction that compares the time he spent running to the time he spent in the park.

Solutions – Brain Aerobics – Week 3 – 7th Grade

1. 27, 15, 15, 16, x

$$\frac{27 + 15 + 15 + 16 + x}{5} = 18$$

$$\frac{73 + x}{5} = 18$$

$$73 + x = 90$$

$$x = 17$$

2. 42

3. 300 + 200 + 100 = 600 total tickets sold

$$\frac{100}{600} = \frac{1}{6}$$

4. 49 – 5 = $44.00

60 x .30 = $18.00

60 – 18 = $42.00

The second backpack is the better value.

5. 3 x 60 = 180 minutes in the park

$$\frac{20}{180} = \frac{1}{9}$$

BRAIN AEROBICS - WEEK 4

1. If an animal can run 40 miles per hour, how many minutes would it take it to run one mile?

2. Susan loved to jump in the plastic balls at the amusement park. She learned that there were 20,000 balls in the bin. Four thousand were red, 3,000 were blue, 5,000 were yellow, and the rest were white. What is the ratio of white balls to the total amount?

3. Sam was driving from San Antonio, Texas to Dallas, Texas. He averaged 60 miles per hour for the first 3 hours and 55 miles per hour for the next 4 hours. How many miles did he drive in 7 hours?

4. Chuck wants to watch the Orange Bowl football game which starts at 8:00 P.M. Eastern Standard Time. He lives in California which is on Pacific Time, 3 hours earlier. Chuck has a 2 hour drive to his friend's house to watch the game. If he leaves at 2:30 P.M., will he arrive at his friend's house in time for the game?

5. If you were born in the year 2000, in what year would you be $\frac{2}{5}$ of a century old?

Solutions – Brain Aerobics – Week 4 – 7th Grade

1. 60 minutes in 1 hour.
$\frac{60}{40}$ = 1.5 minutes

2. 20,000 – 4,000 – 3,000 – 5,000 = 8,000 white balls
$\frac{8,000}{20,000} = \frac{2}{5}$

3. 60 x 3 = 180 miles
55 x 4 = 220 miles
180 + 220 = 400 miles

4. 8:00 – 3 hrs. = 5:00 The game begins at 5:00 Pacific Time.
2:30 + 2:00 = 4:30 Chuck will arrive at his friend's house at 4:30 so he will arrive in time for the game.

5. 1 century = 100 years
$100 \times \frac{2}{5} = \frac{200}{5}$ = 40 years
2000 + 40 = 2040

BRAIN AEROBICS - WEEK 5

1. Light travels at the speed of 186,000 miles per second. If you could travel at the speed of light, how many round trips could you make from Detroit to Miami in 2 seconds if the distance from Detroit to Miami is approximately 1200 miles?

2. Peter walks $\frac{1}{8}$ of a mile in $2\frac{1}{2}$ minutes. How many miles will he walk in 2 hours?

3. Keeko could fly her kite 560 feet in the air. Kevin's kite flew at an altitude 150% higher than Keeko's. How high did Kevin's kite fly?

4. This number is greater than 10 and less than 100. It is a palindrome. It is divisible by 3. The sum of its digits equals 12. What is the number?

5. Jim rode 125 kilometers on his bike trip. Juan's trip was $\frac{4}{5}$ as long as Jim's trip. How many kilometers did Juan ride?

Solutions – Brain Aerobics – Week 5 – 7th Grade

1. 1200 x 2 = 2,400 miles in one round trip
186,000 x 2 = 372,000 miles (amount of miles you could travel in 2 seconds)

$\frac{372,000}{2,400}$ = 155 round trips

2. 2 hours = 120 minutes

120 ÷ 2.5 = 48

48 x $\frac{1}{8}$ = $\frac{48}{8}$ = 6 miles

3. 150% = 1.50 = 1.5
560 x 1.50 = 840 feet
560 + 840 = 1400 feet

4. 66

5. 125 x $\frac{4}{5}$ = $\frac{500}{5}$ = 100 kilometers

BRAIN AEROBICS - WEEK 6

1. A group of hikers climbed to the top of a mountain. They climbed 2,000 feet each day for five days to get to the top. Approximately how many miles tall was the mountain?

2. Twin prime numbers are prime numbers that have a difference of 2. (example: 11 & 13) These twin prime numbers are greater than 30 and less than 50. The product of the digits of the first number equals 4, and the product of the digits of the second number equals 12. What are the twin prime numbers?

3. Partners in a business decided to share the year's profits according to how long each partner had been with the company. Five partners received $\frac{1}{3}$, $\frac{1}{4}$, $\frac{1}{6}$, $\frac{1}{8}$, and $\frac{1}{12}$ of the profits respectively. The sixth partner received $1,000. How much money did each partner receive?

4. The 2000 winter Olympics were held in Sydney, Australia. Sydney is 15 hours later than New York City in time (except during the months of daylight savings time). If it is 10:00 P.M. Saturday, February 5th in New York, what time is it in Sydney?

5. Samantha's college tuition for one year was $3,600. The cost is going to increase by $\frac{1}{8}$ next year. What will be the cost of her tuition next year?

Solutions – Brain Aerobics – Week 6 – 7th Grade

1. $2{,}000 \times 5 = 10{,}000$ feet
1 mile = 5,280 feet
$10{,}000 \div 5{,}280 \approx 2$ miles

2. 41 and 43

3. Use 24 as a common denominator.

$\frac{8}{24} + \frac{6}{24} + \frac{4}{24} + \frac{3}{24} + \frac{2}{24} = \frac{23}{24}$ so there is $\frac{1}{24}$ left

$\frac{1}{24} = \$1{,}000$ $\quad \frac{8}{24} = \frac{1}{3} = \$8{,}000$ $\quad \frac{3}{24} = \frac{1}{8} = \$3{,}000$

$\frac{6}{24} = \frac{1}{4} = \$6{,}000$ $\quad \frac{2}{24} = \frac{1}{12} = \$2{,}000$

$\frac{4}{24} = \frac{1}{6} = \$4{,}000$

4. 1:00 p.m. Sunday February 6th

5. $\$3{,}600 \times \frac{1}{8} = \frac{\$3{,}600}{8} = \$450$

$\$3{,}600 + \$450 = \$4{,}050.00$

BRAIN AEROBICS - WEEK 7

1. A recycling station brought in $\frac{1}{2}$ ton of newspapers on Monday. On Tuesday the station collected only half of what it did on Monday. On Wednesday the station collected only half of what it did on Tuesday. How many pounds did it collect in total during the three days?

2. The distance between Greenville and St. Clair is 5 kilometers. The distance between these two cities is $\frac{1}{5}$ of the distance between Greenville and Sunnyvale. How many kilometers are between Greenville and Sunnyvale?

3. If you add $\frac{1}{3}$, $\frac{1}{4}$, and $\frac{1}{8}$ of a number together you get 585. What is the number? (Round your answer to the nearest hundredth.)

4. Which is the better value? A skateboard that costs $150 with a 50% discount, or the same skateboard with a 30% discount off the original $150 price, then a 25% discount off the discounted price?

5. Find the set of counting numbers which would make this equation true.
   $x + 3 \rangle 10$

Solutions – Brain Aerobics – Week 7 – 7th Grade

1. 1 ton = 2,000 pounds

$\frac{1}{2}$ ton = 1,000 pounds

1,000 + 500 + 250 = 1,750 pounds total

2. X = the distance between Greenville and Sunnyvale

$X \bullet \frac{1}{5} = 5$

$X \bullet .20 = 5$

$X = \frac{5}{.2}$

X = 25 km

3. $\frac{1}{3}x + \frac{1}{4}x + \frac{1}{8}x = 585$

$\frac{8}{24}x + \frac{6}{24}x + \frac{3}{24}x = 585$

$\frac{17}{24}x = 585$

$17x = 14{,}040$

$x = 825.88$

4. 150 x .5 = \$75.00

150 – \$75 = \$75.00

150 x .30 = \$45.00

150 – \$45 = \$105

105 x .25 = \$26.25

105 – \$26.25 = \$78.75

50% off is the better value.

5.
$$\begin{array}{r} x + 3 > 10 \\ -3 \quad -3 \\ \hline x > 7 \end{array}$$

BRAIN AEROBICS - WEEK 8

1. Carl rode his bike 27 mph for the first 2 hours of his bike trip, then rode 24 mph for the last 2 hours. How many more miles did he travel in the first 2 hours than the last 2 hours?

2. Sadie has a drawer filled with equal amounts of pink, purple, yellow, and green socks. If she draws socks out of the drawer one at a time, how many socks will she have to pull out before she has a matched pair?

3. Lana's class held a lottery to see which child got to take the pinata home to fill with candy. Lana heard that the winning number was a prime number, and she held the number 19. What is the probability that Lana held the winning number if there are 23 students in the class?

4. Earl bought a car for $5400. In two years the car depreciated in value by $\frac{1}{6}$. What was the car worth after two years?

5. Sondra went to a conference where she learned that 20% of the 60 people in attendance were from the U.S. She also found out that 25% of the people from the U.S. were from California. How many people were from the United States, but not from California?

Solutions – Brain Aerobics – Week 8 – 7th Grade

1. 27 x 2 = 54
24 x 2 = 48
54 - 48 = 6 miles

2. At least 2
At most 5

3. There are 9 prime numbers between 1 and 23.
{2, 3, 5, 7, 11, 13, 17, 19, 23}
$\frac{1}{9}$

4. $\$5,400 \times \frac{1}{6} = \frac{\$5,400}{6} = \$900$

$5400 – $900 = $4,500

5. 60 x .20 = 12 people from the U.S.
12 x .25 = 3 people from California
12 – 3 = 9 people from the U.S., but not from California

BRAIN AEROBICS - WEEK 9

1. William notices that the number on his car's odometer is 2442. He realizes that this number is a palindrome. How many miles will he have to drive to get to the next palindrome on his odometer?

2. Fifteen years ago Derrick was $\frac{1}{4}$ the age he is today. How old is Derrick?

3. The trivia contest on the radio had a jackpot valued at $180. The first place winner received $\frac{2}{3}$ of the prize and the second place winner received $\frac{1}{6}$ of the prize. The remaining money was split between the two winners who tied for third place. How much money did each third place winner receive?

4. Jesse was making a casserole that called for 2 cups of cheese for 12 servings. He needed to make enough to serve only 8 people. How much cheese did he need?

5. For Grandpa Joe's 70th birthday, all of his grandchildren decided to buy him a new camera that cost $240. They had $180 saved. What percentage of the total cost of the camera had they saved? What percentage of the total amount did they still need?

Solutions – Brain Aerobics – Week 9 – 7th Grade

1. The next palindrome in miles will be 2552.
2552 – 2442 = 110 miles

2. $x - 15 = \frac{1}{4}x$
$-15 = \frac{1}{4}x - x$
$-15 = -\frac{3}{4}x$
$-60 = -3x$
$20 = x$

3. $180 \times \frac{2}{3} = \frac{360}{3} = \$120$ first place
$180 \times \frac{1}{6} = \frac{180}{6} = \$30$ second place
180 – 120 – 30 = \$30
30 ÷ 2 = \$15 each for third place

4. $\frac{2}{12} = \frac{x}{8} \quad \frac{16}{12} = \frac{12x}{12}$
$1\frac{4}{12} = x$
$1\frac{1}{3} = x$

5. \$240 x p = \$180
$p = \frac{180}{240}$ p = percent
p = .75 = 75% saved
They still needed 25%.

BRAIN AEROBICS - WEEK 10

1. If it is 2:15 P.M. and you were told to move the minute hand of the clock 270 degrees clockwise, what time would it be?

2. Bob used a jar to collect his marbles . He had 15 white marbles, 20 green marbles, 10 red marbles, 15 black marbles, and 30 blue marbles. What fraction of the total number of marbles are the black and white ones?

3. Charlene was in a sales job that paid on commission. The first year she earned $15,000. Her goal for the second year was to increase her salary by 100%. How much money was she hoping to earn in her second year?

4. Of the 1,200 concert tickets sold, $\frac{1}{2}$ sold for $20.00, $\frac{1}{4}$ sold for $10.00, and the rest sold for $5.00. How many tickets sold for $5.00?

5. A guitar and case costs $150.00. The guitar costs $100 more than the case. How much does the case cost?

Solutions – Brain Aerobics – Week 10 – 7th Grade

1.

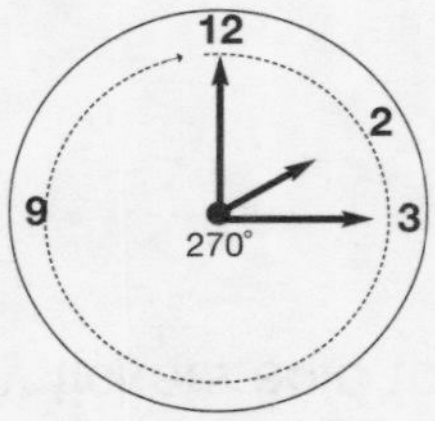

3:00 p.m.

2. 15 + 20 + 10 + 15 + 30 = 90 marbles total
15 + 15 = 30 black and white marbles
$\frac{30}{90} = \frac{1}{3}$

3. 100% of \$15,000 is \$15,000.
\$15,000 + \$15,000 = \$30,000

4. $\frac{1}{2} + \frac{1}{4} + \frac{1}{4}$ = all tickets sold so $\frac{1}{4}$ of the tickets sold for \$5.00.
1200 x $\frac{1}{4} = \frac{1200}{4}$ = 300 tickets

5. x = cost of the case
x + 100 = cost of the guitar
x + (x + 100) = \$150.00
2x + 100 = \$150
2x = \$50
x = \$25.00
case = \$25.00
guitar = \$125.00

The Metric Units

Temperature - Celsius
- 0°C: the freezing point of water
- 37°C: the normal body temperature
- 100°C: the boiling point of water

Mass
- 1000 milligrams (mg) = 1 gram
- 1000 grams = 1 kilogram (kg)
- 1000 kilograms = 1 metric ton (t)

Capacity
- 1000 milliliters (mL) = 1 liter (L)
- 1000 liters = 1 kiloliter (kL)

Length
- 10 millimeters (mm) = 1 centimeter
- 10 centimeters (cm) = 1 decimeter
- 1000 millimeters (mm) = 1 meter (m)
- 100 centimeters = 1 meter (m)
- 10 decimeters (dm) = 1 meter
- 1000 meters (m) = 1 kilometer (km)

The Customary Units

Temperature - Fahrenheit
- 32°F: the freezing point of water
- 98.6°F: the normal body temperature
- 212°F: the boiling point of water

Weight
- 1 pound (lb) = 16 ounces (oz)
- 1 ton = 2,000 pounds

Time
- 1 minute (min) = 60 seconds (s)
- 1 hour = 60 minutes
- 1 day = 24 hours
- 1 week = 7 days
- 1 month (mo) = approx. 4 weeks
- 1 year (yr) = 365 days, 52 weeks, 12 months
- 1 decade = 10 years
- 1 century = 100 years

Capacity

1 cup (c) =	8 fluid ounces (fl oz)
1 pint (pt) =	16 fluid ounces 2 cups
1 quart (qt) =	32 fluid ounces 4 cups 2 pints
1 gallon (gal)=	128 fluid ounces 16 cups 8 pints 4 quarts

Length

1 foot (ft) =	12 inches (in)
1 yard (yd) =	36 inches 3 feet
1 mile (mi) =	5,280 feet 1,760 yards

GLOSSARY OF TERMS AND FORMULAS

a.m.: a way of expressing time between 12:00 midnight and 12:00 noon.

absolute value: the positive distance from zero.

acute angle: an angle measuring less than 90 degrees.

addends: numbers to be added together in an addition problem.

algebraic expression: a combination of numbers and variables joined by the operations of arithmetic.

angle: the union of two rays (the sides) at a point (the vertex).

area: the number of square units or parts of square units required to cover a two-dimensional figure.

Formula examples: parallelogram: $A = hb$ trapezoid: $A = \frac{1}{2}h(b_1 + b_2)$

triangle: $A = \frac{1}{2}hb$ rectangle: $A = lw$

circle: $A = \pi r^2$ square: $A = s^2$

arithmetic sequence: a number pattern where the difference between consecutive numbers (terms) is constant.

average: a number obtained by adding a group of numbers together and dividing by the number of addends.

biased sample: one in which members of a sample are underrepresented or totally ignored.

center: the point from which all points on a circle are equally distant.

circle: the set of all points equally distanct (the radius) from a point (the center).

circumference: the distance around a circle.

Formula: $c = 2\pi r$ where r = radius $\pi \approx 3.14$

common denominator: a multiple of all denominators in a problem.

common factor: a number that is a factor of two other numbers is a common factor.

Example: 3 is a common factor of 9 and 12.

common multiple: a number that is a multiple of two other numbers.

Example: 24 is a common multiple of 6 and 4.

complementary angles: two angles with a sum of 90 degrees.

congruent: refers to figures that have the same shape and size.

congruent figure: the image of another figure under a translation, reflection or rotation.

coordinates: number pairs used in graphing. The horizontal axis is listed first and the vertical axis is listed second.

Example: 8, 10

customary measurement: units of measurement used in the United States.
Example: feet, pounds, miles, etc.

cylinder: a solid object with two identical circular ends (think of a soup can).

decade: a period of 10 years.

decimal point: a period put just before the decimal fraction such as the periods in .625 and .08.

degree: a unit used to measure an angle or temperature.

degrees Celsius (C°): metric unit of measurement for temperature.

degrees Fahrenheit (F°): customary unit of measurement for temperature.

denominator: number below the line in a fraction.
Example: $\frac{1}{2}$ ⇐denominator

diameter: a segment connecting two points on a circle that contains the center.

difference: the answer to a subtraction problem.

digits: symbols used to write numbers.
Example: 6, 7, 8, etc.

divisor: a number by which another number is to be divided. When you divide the number 6 by 2, 2 is the divisor.

equal: when two or more numbers or items are the same in value, size or number.

equation: occurs when two expressions are joined by an = sign.

estimate: to find an answer that is close to the exact answer.

even number: a number that has 0, 2, 4, 6, or 8 in the one's place.

expanded form: a way to write numbers to show the place value of each digit.
Example: 1,322 = 1,000 + 300 + 20 + 2

exponent: is a number that shows how many times a base is used as a factor.
Ex. $x^3 = x \times x \times x$

factor: any one of the numbers that when multiplied gives a product.
Example: 4 x 5 = 20

fraction: a number that represents part of a set or region.

formula: an equation that states that a single variable is equal to an expression made up of one or more different variables.

function: a relationship where each member of the domain is paired with exactly one member of the range.

greater than (>): a way to show that one number is larger than another.
Example: 9 > 2 means "9 is greater than 2."

greatest common factor: the largest number that can be a factor of each of two other numbers.

hypotenuse: the side opposite the right angle in a right triangle.

integer: any whole number and its opposite.

interest: a fee paid for the privilege of borrowing money.

intersecting: the point or points that are the same for two sets of points or elements.

Example: 

inverse operation: the "opposite" operation.

Example: addition is the inverse of subtraction.

irrational numbers: a number that cannot be written as a quotient (fraction).

Example: π, $\sqrt{2}$

least common denominator (LCD): the lowest common multiple of two or more denominators.

least common multiple (LCM): the lowest number (not a zero) that is a multiple of two given numbers.

less than (<): a way to show one number is smaller than another.

Example: $2 < 9$ means "2 is less than 9."

line: a series of points that extends in opposite directions without end.

line segment: a part of a line that has two endpoints.

lowest terms: a fraction when the numerator and denominator have no common factor larger than 1.

mean: the average of a data set.

median: the middle number in a set of numbers when that set is arranged in order. When there is not a middle number, the median is the average of the two middle numbers.

mental math: performing calculations in a person's head without pencil or paper.

metrics: unit of measurement.

Example: centimeters, kilograms, milliliters

mixed number: a combination of a whole number and a fraction.

Example: $3\frac{1}{2}$

multiple: the product of a number and any non-zero number.

negative number: a number that is less than zero.

number line: a line that shows where numbers fall in order.

Example: 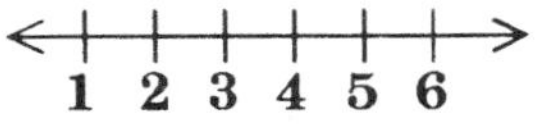

number sentence: occurs when two expressions are joined by a math verb.

Examples of math verbs are =, ≤, ≥, <, and >.

numerator: the number above the line in a fraction.

Example: $\frac{5}{8}$ ⇐numerator

numeral: number

numerical expression: an expression that contains two or more numbers.

Example: 6 + 2

obtuse angle: an angle measuring more than 90 degrees.

odd number: a whole number containing 1, 3, 5, 7, or 9 in the one's place.

opposites: two numbers that are the same distance from zero on the number line. The sum of opposites is zero.

Example: -1 + 1 = 0

outlier: a number that varies widely from the rest of a data set.

p.m.: a way of expressing time from 12:00 noon to 12:00 midnight.

parallel: two lines in the same plane that do not intersect or are the same.

Example: 

parallelogram: a quadrilateral with opposite sides parallel.

Example: 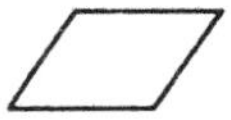 or 

percent: %, times $\frac{1}{100}$, per 100.

perfect square: the square of an integer.

Example: since $2^2 = 4$, 4 is a perfect square.

perimeter: the distance around a figure (the sum of all its sides).

perpendicular lines: two lines that intersect (cross) and form right angles (90° angles).

Example: 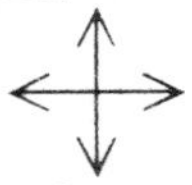

place value: the value given to the place a digit occupies in a number.

Example: 427 (4 is in the hundreds place, 2 is in the tens place and 7 is in the ones place.)

polygon: a figure formed by three or more line segments, each of which intersects exactly two others at their endpoints, to make a closed figure.

polynomial: an expression containing one or more terms.

positive number: a number that is more than zero.

profit: money received from a business venture after all expenses have been paid.

predict: to guess what will happen.

prime number: a number greater than 1 that can only be divided evenly by itself and the number 1.

prism: a three-dimensional figure with rectangular or parallelogram sides and parallel, congruent bases.

probability: is the number of favorable outcomes divided by the number of possible outcomes, when all outcomes are equally likely to occur.

product: the answer to a multiplication problem.

proportion: equal rates or ratios.

pyramid: a three-dimensional figure with triangular sides that meet at a vertex and a base that is a polygon.

Pythagorean theorem: in a right triangle, the square of the hypotenuse is equal to the sum of the squares of the other two sides (legs).

Formula: $a^2 + b^2 = c^2$

quadrilateral: a polygon with four sides.

quotient: the answer to a division problem (other than a remainder).

radius: a segment from the center of a circle to a point on that circle.

Example: 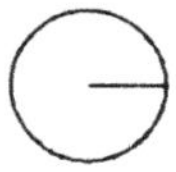

random sample: a population sample where each member of a population is equally likely to be chosen and where each member is chosen independently of any other member.

rate: when x and y are different quantities, then $\frac{x}{y}$ is the amount of x per y.

ratio: the quotient of two numbers that are in the same units. Written $n : m$ or $\frac{n}{m}$.

rational number: a number that can be written as the ratio of two integers (a fraction).

ray: a line that consists of an endpoint and all the points of a line on one side of the endpoint.

real number: any number that can be represented as a terminating, repeating, or infinite decimal.

reciprocal: the reciprocal of a number, n, is $\frac{1}{n}$. The product of any number and its reciprocal is 1.

reflection: a transformation in which each point is mapped onto its reflection image over a line. A reflection figure and its image are congruent.

remainder: the number that is left over when a number cannot be divided evenly.

Example: if you divide 7 by 3, the answer is 2 with a "remainder of 1."

rhombus: a quadrilateral with four equal sides.

right angle: an angle measuring 90 degrees.

right triangle: a triangle that has one right angle.

rounding: expressing a quantity as its nearest multiple of ten. Numbers 1-4 are rounded down. Number 5-9 are rounded up.
Example: 32 rounded to the nearest ten is 30.
Example: 37 rounded to the nearest ten is 40.

sale price: a price that is lower than the original price for an item.

sales tax: an amount of money added to the price of an item that is paid to the government.

sequence: an ordered list.

set: a group of items.

slope: (also called *tilt*) is the ratio of the $\frac{rise}{run}$ of a line. The formula for slope, m, is $m = \frac{y_2 - y_1}{x_2 - x_1}$

solution: a value for a variable that makes a number sentence (equation) true.

square: a figure with 4 right angles and 4 equal sides.

square root: $\sqrt{\ }$ a number that when multiplied by itself will produce a certain number.
Example: the square root of 25 is 5.

standard form: the way in which numbers are usually written.
Example: 6,852

sum: the answer to an addition problem.

supplementary angle: two angles with a sum of 180°.

tip: an amount of money paid to a person such as a wait person to say "thank-you" for good service, usually determined as a percentage of the total bill.

transformation: is a change. A reflection, rotation, and translation results in a change where the preimage and the image are congruent. A size change results in a change where the image is larger or smaller than the preimage.

translation: (also called a *slide*) is a horizontal move of h units and a vertical move of v units. A translation image and its image are congruent.

trapezoid: a quadrilateral with one pair of opposite sides parallel.

Example: 

triangle: a polygon with 3 sides.

value: the worth of a number.

variable: a symbol that can be replaced by another.

volume: the amount of space occupied by an object, expressed in cubic units.
Formula: length x width x height

whole number: any number 0, 1, 2, 3, etc.

1.) a. $2\frac{1}{2} = 2\frac{2}{4}$, $+3\frac{3}{4} = 3\frac{3}{4}$, $5\frac{5}{4} = 6\frac{1}{4}$
b. $1\frac{2}{3} = 1\frac{4}{6}$, $+6\frac{5}{6} = 6\frac{5}{6}$, $7\frac{9}{6} = 8\frac{3}{6} = 8\frac{1}{2}$
c. $2\frac{11}{12} = 2\frac{11}{12}$, $+\frac{5}{6} = \frac{10}{12}$, $2\frac{21}{12} = 3\frac{9}{12} = 3\frac{3}{4}$

2.) a. .25 b. .75 c. .4 d. .3 e. .7 f. .5

3.) $\frac{4}{15} \times \frac{15}{8} = \frac{1}{2}$

4.) a. 0
b. $18 \div 3 \times 2 =$ $6 \times 2 = 12$
c. $3^2 - 3 \div 3 =$ $9 - 3 \div 3 =$ $9 - 1 = 8$

5.) $\frac{36 \text{ concepts}}{\text{min.}} \times \frac{15 \text{ min.}}{1} = 540$ concepts

6.) a. $\frac{2}{3}$ b. $\frac{2}{3} = \frac{5}{x}$ $15 = 2x$ (7.5 cups)

7.) $.09\overline{)83.88}$ = 932.
−81, 28, −27, 18, −18

8.) a. $3 + -2 = 1$ b. $3 - (-2) = 3 + 2 = 5$ c. $3(-2) = -6$
d. $3^2 = 9$ e. $\frac{3}{-2} = \frac{-3}{2}$ f. $(-2)^2 = 4$

9.) A = (2,4) B = (5,−2) C = (−5,−2) D = (−3,2)

10.) a. C b. B
A = 3 times
B = 2 times
C = 4 times
D = 3 times

11.) .001 when dividing by 100 move decimal 2 places to the left. .001

12.) a. 16 oz = 1 pound
1600 oz = 100 pounds
b. answers will vary
924.50 × 1600 = \$1,479,200.00

1.) 3 quarters = \$.75
3 dimes = \$.30
4 nickels = \$.20
\$1.25
x% of \$5.00 = \$1.25
\$1.25 ÷ \$5.00 = .25 = 25%

2.) a. $3\frac{3}{4} = 3\frac{3}{4}$, $-1\frac{1}{2} = 1\frac{2}{4}$, $2\frac{1}{4}$
b. $2\frac{3}{8} = 2\frac{3}{8} = 1\frac{11}{8}$, $-1\frac{3}{4} = 1\frac{6}{8} = 1\frac{6}{8}$, $\frac{5}{8}$
c. $9\frac{1}{8} = 9\frac{1}{8} = 8\frac{9}{8}$, $-3\frac{1}{2} = 3\frac{4}{8} = 3\frac{4}{8}$, $5\frac{5}{8}$

3.) $2^0 = 1$ $2^1 = 2$ $2^2 = 4$ $2^3 = 8$ $2^4 = 16$ $2^5 = 32$
$2^6 = 64$ $2^7 = 128$ $2^8 = 256$ $2^9 = 512$ $2^{10} = 1{,}024$

4.) $\frac{5}{6} = \frac{5}{6}$, $+\frac{1}{3} = \frac{2}{6}$, $\frac{7}{6} = 1\frac{1}{6}$

5.) 4 qts. = 1 gallon
2 pts. = 1 quart
$2\frac{1}{2}$ gallons × $\frac{4 \text{ qts.}}{1 \text{ gallon}}$ = 10 qts.
10 qts. × $\frac{2 \text{ pints}}{1 \text{ qt}}$ = 20 pts.

6.) a. 50% b. 80% c. 8% d. 60% e. 33% f. 100%

7.) 400 × 100 = 40,000

8.) $3^2 = 3 \times 3 = 9$ 100 ÷ 10 = 10
8% of 100 = 8 $\frac{77}{11} = 7$
Correct: $\frac{77}{11}$, 8% of 100, 3^2, 100 ÷ 10

9.) a. $\frac{36}{50}$
b. $\frac{36}{50} \times \frac{x}{500}$
50x = 18000
x = 360 students

10.) $A = 2\frac{1}{2} \times 3\frac{3}{4}$
$\frac{5}{2} \times \frac{15}{4} = \frac{75}{8} = 9\frac{3}{8}$ sq. ft.

11.) a. 15, 30, 45 b. 2, 3, 5 c. 11, 13, 17, 19, 23

12.) 1.06 × \$2,864 = \$3,035.84

1.) 1+2+3+4…+31 = \$496.00

2.) a. $2\frac{1}{2} \times 3 = \frac{5}{2} \times 3 = \frac{15}{2} = 7\frac{1}{2}$
b. $1\frac{3}{4} \times \frac{1}{7} = \frac{7}{4} \times \frac{1}{7} = \frac{1}{4}$
c. $\frac{2}{3} \times \frac{3}{5} \times \frac{2}{9} = \frac{4}{45}$

3.) ten thousandths

4.) 75 × 10,000 = 750,000
when multiplying by 10,000 move decimal point to the right 4 places

5.) $1\frac{1}{12} = 1\frac{1}{12}$, $+\frac{1}{3} = \frac{4}{12}$, $1\frac{5}{12}$
$1\frac{3}{4} = 1\frac{9}{12}$, $+\frac{1}{3} = \frac{4}{12}$, $1\frac{13}{12} = 2\frac{1}{12}$

6.) $\frac{8 \text{ min.}}{\text{hour}} \times \frac{1 \text{ hour}}{60 \text{ min.}} \times \frac{5280 \text{ ft.}}{1 \text{ mile}} =$
$\frac{42240 \text{ ft.}}{60 \text{ min.}} = \frac{704 \text{ ft.}}{\text{min.}}$

7.) $A = \left(\frac{2}{3}\right)^2 = \frac{4}{9}$ in²

8.) a. $\frac{5}{100} = 5\%$
b. $\frac{5}{25} = \frac{20}{100} = 20\%$
c. $\frac{5}{10} = \frac{50}{100} = 50\%$
d. $\frac{5}{50} = \frac{10}{100} = 10\%$

9.) $37\overline{)5,217}$ = 141
−37, 151, −148, 37, −37

10.) a. 19, 22
b. 13 − 10 = 3
c. 40

11.) $\frac{1}{2}(32) = 16$ = cat
$\frac{1}{4}(16) = 4$ = parrot
4 lbs

12.) $\frac{1}{3} = .3333\overline{3}$ 30% = .3000 .33330 $\frac{33}{100} = .33000$
30% $\frac{33}{100}$ .3333 $\frac{1}{3}$

1.) a. $7\frac{1}{6} = 7\frac{1}{6} = 6\frac{7}{6}$, $-3\frac{1}{2} = 3\frac{3}{6} = 3\frac{3}{6}$, $3\frac{4}{6} = 3\frac{2}{3}$
b. $5\frac{1}{4} \div 3\frac{1}{2} = \frac{21}{4} \div \frac{7}{2}$
$\frac{21}{4} \times \frac{2}{7} = \frac{3}{2} = 1\frac{1}{2}$

2.) $.7\overline{)77.7}$ = 111.

3.) a. $1\frac{2}{3} \div \frac{5}{6} =$ $\frac{5}{3} \times \frac{6}{5} = 2$
b. $4\frac{1}{2} \div 2\frac{3}{4} =$ $\frac{9}{2} \div \frac{11}{4}$ $\frac{9}{2} \times \frac{4}{11} = \frac{18}{11} = 1\frac{7}{11}$
c. $-\frac{4}{9} \div \frac{2}{3} =$ $\frac{4}{9} \times \frac{3}{2} = -\frac{2}{3}$

4.) $7\frac{6}{5} = 8\frac{1}{5}$

5.) a. 3+5×2 < 5×3+2
3+10 = 13; 15+2 = 17
b. 5×5−3 > 5×(5−3)
25−3 = 22; 5×2 = 10
c. 10−2×5 = 2×5−10
10−10 = 0; 10−10 = 0
d. 5−(5+5) < 5−5+5
5−10 = −5; 0+5 = 5

6.) $A = \frac{1}{2}(6.3)(2.2) = 6.93$ in²

7.) L = 3 W = 1.5
3 × 1.5 = 4.5 sq. in.

8.) a. $\frac{100}{115} = \frac{1050}{x}$
b. $\frac{100x}{100} = \frac{120{,}750}{100}$
x = 1207.5 standard miles

9.) 50 + 102 + 25 = 177

10.) a. $4 \times \frac{1}{4} = 1$ b. $-\frac{1}{3}x - 3 = 1$ c. $\left(\frac{2}{3}\right)\left(\frac{3}{2}\right) = 1$
d. $\frac{1}{n} \cdot n = 1$ e. 1

11.) $7\frac{1}{4}$

1.) a. $1\frac{1}{4}=\frac{5}{4}$ $\frac{3}{4}+\square=\frac{5}{4}$ $\square=\frac{2}{4}=(\frac{1}{2})$

b. $1\frac{1}{2}=\frac{3}{2}=\frac{6}{4}$ $\frac{6}{4}-\square=\frac{5}{4}$ $\square=(\frac{1}{4})$

2.) $7.6\overline{)630.8}$ = (83.)
−608
228
−228

3.) (.8)

4.) $\frac{4}{5}=.80$

a. $\frac{30}{60}=\frac{1}{2}=.50$ (b.) .82 c. $45\%=\frac{45}{100}=.45$

5.) a. $\frac{1.27 \text{ dollars}}{1 \text{ Euro}}, \frac{40 \text{ dollars}}{X \text{ Euros}}$ $40=1.27x$ 31.496 Euros = X round to (31.50 Euros)

b. $\frac{1.27}{1}=\frac{x}{28}$ x = ($35.56)

6.) a. $\frac{20 \text{ cards divisible by 5}}{100 \text{ cards in deck}}=(\frac{1}{5}$ or 1:5)

b. $\frac{5 \text{ cards divisible by 20}}{100 \text{ cards in deck}}=(\frac{1}{20}$ or 1:20)

7.) 1,100 ft. x 10 sec. = 11,000 ft.
11,000 ÷ 5,280 (ft. per mile) (about 2 miles)

8.) $A=3.14\ (4.8)^2$
$A=72.3456\approx$ (72.3 cm^2)

9.) a. $y=2x$ (0,0) (1,2) (2,4)

b.
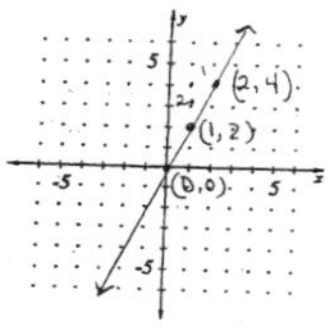

c. $\frac{2}{1}=2$

10.) a. 9 → (3)(3)
b. 18 → (2) 9 → (3)(3)
c. 36 → (2) 18 → (2) 9 → (3)(3)
d. 2x2x3x3 = (36)

11.) a. $\frac{25}{80}=\frac{10}{32}$ b. $\frac{18}{48}=\frac{15}{40}$ c. $\frac{2}{3}=\frac{10}{16}$

800 = 800 (T) 720 = 720 (T) 30 ≠ (F) 32

1.) a. 632 x500 (316,000) b. 2.34 x.003 .00702 (.00702)

2.) a. $8\frac{1}{8}=7\frac{9}{8}$
$-4\frac{5}{8}=4\frac{5}{8}$
$3\frac{4}{8}=(3\frac{1}{2})$

b. $\frac{2}{3}=\frac{8}{12}$
$+\frac{1}{12}=\frac{1}{12}$
$\frac{9}{12}=(\frac{3}{4})$

3.) $\frac{1}{2}=\frac{x \text{ in}}{18}$
$2x=18$
$x=$ (9 in.)

4.) 75 = 3x25 125 = 5x25 50 = 2x25 3, 5, 2 all prime numbers so (25)

5.) a. 510 = 500+10 $\frac{1}{2}$ of 500 = 250
$\frac{1}{2}$ of 10 = +5
(255)

b. 1,080 = 1,000 + 80 $\frac{1}{2}$ of 1000 = 500
$\frac{1}{2}$ of 80 = +40
(540)

c. 860 = 800+60 $\frac{1}{2}$ of 800 = 400
$\frac{1}{2}$ of 60 = +30
(430)

6.) (463)

7.) 6+(−12) = (−6)

8.) 1 liter = 1,000 ml
(32 x 1,000 = 32,000 ml)

9.) a. 36,000 ↑ 40,000 (1,940,000)
b. 936,000 ↓ 900,000 (1,900,000)
c. 1,936,743 ↑ (2,000,000)

10.) a $1\frac{4}{5}\times1\frac{2}{3}=\frac{9}{5}\times\frac{5}{3}=\frac{3}{1}=(3)$

b. $\frac{2}{3}\div\frac{8}{9}$ $\frac{2}{3}\times\frac{9}{8}=(\frac{3}{4})$

11.) $\frac{12 \text{ words}}{\text{min.}}\times.50=\frac{6 \text{ words}}{\text{min.}}$ $\frac{12 \text{ words}}{\text{min}}+\frac{6 \text{ words}}{\text{min.}}=\frac{18 \text{ words}}{\text{min.}}$

$\frac{18 \text{ words}}{\text{min.}}\times.50=\frac{9 \text{ words}}{\text{min}}$ $\frac{18 \text{ words}}{\text{min.}}+\frac{9 \text{ words}}{\text{min.}}=(\frac{27 \text{ words}}{\text{min.}})$

12.) (37.190016)

1.) a. $3\frac{1}{7}\div5\frac{1}{2}=\frac{22}{7}\div\frac{11}{2}$
$\frac{22}{7}\times\frac{2}{11}=(\frac{4}{7})$

b. $2\frac{2}{3}\times3\frac{1}{8}=\frac{8}{3}\times\frac{25}{8}=\frac{25}{3}=(8\frac{1}{3})$

2.) a. p = 4+2.8+4+2.8 = (13.6 in.)
b. A = 4.2 = (8 in^2)

3.) ($6.00)

4.) 45.107
+27.894
73.(00)1

5.) $50.7\overline{)1662.96}$ = (32.8)
−1521
1419
−1014
4056
−4056

6.) change fractions to decimals to compare
$\frac{2}{3}=.6\bar{6}$ $\frac{3}{4}=.75$
so (−7, −5, −3, $-\frac{1}{6}, \frac{2}{3}, \frac{3}{4}$)

7.) what percent of
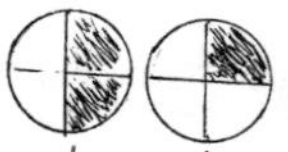
$\frac{1}{2}$ $\frac{1}{4}$
(50%)

8.) 350
x .80
(280.00)

9.) .773 ↓ (.77)

10.) a. $\frac{800}{1000}=\frac{8}{10}=.8=(80\%)$

b. .8 x 200,000 = (160,000 people)

11.) a. h = 0 1 2 3 4 5 h
w = 0 5.00 10.00 15.00 20.00 25.00 5.00h

b. w = (5.00h)

c. w = 5.00 x 5 x 6 = ($150)

1.) $4\frac{1}{3}$
$+1\frac{2}{3}$
$5\frac{3}{3}=(6)$

2.) a. $1\frac{7}{8}\times2\frac{2}{5}=\frac{15}{8}\times\frac{12}{5}=\frac{9}{2}=(4\frac{1}{2})$

b. $\frac{3}{4}\div\frac{1}{8}=\frac{3}{4}\times\frac{8}{1}=\frac{6}{1}=(6)$

3.) (4,000,000 + 6,000 + 80)

4.) a. $12\overline{)\$414.72}$ = ($34.56)
−36
54
−48
67
−60
72
−72

b. 12.85
x 0.34
5140
3855
(4.3690)

5.) a. 6 → (2)(3) b. 10 → (2)(5) c. 20 → (2) 10 → (2)(5)
d. 2x2x3x5 = (60)

6.) change fractions to decimals to compare $-\frac{1}{3}=-.33\bar{3}$, $\frac{2}{5}=.40$, $-\frac{1}{4}=-.25$
$\frac{2}{3}=.66\bar{6}$, $\frac{5}{6}=.8\bar{3}$, $\frac{5}{8}=.625$
so ($-\frac{1}{3}, -\frac{1}{4}, \frac{2}{5}, \frac{5}{8}, \frac{2}{3}, \frac{5}{6}$)

7.) a. (3) b. (2) c. (8)

8.) 1:57
−1:46
:11 between each time

1:57
+:11
1:68 = (2:08)

2:19
+:11
(2:30)

9.) 1 ton = 2,000 lbs.
10,000 lbs · 1 ton / 2,000 lbs =
$\frac{10{,}000 \text{ tons}}{2{,}000}$ = (5 tons)

10.) 150% = 1.5
800
x 1.5
4000
800
(1,200.0)

11.) $5,700
x .09
$513.00

$5,700
+513
($6,213)

12.) $\frac{93{,}000{,}000 \text{ mi}}{186{,}000 \text{ sec}}$
500 sec x $\frac{1 \text{ min}}{60 \text{ sec}}$ = (8.$\bar{3}$ min)

1.) a. $-\frac{3}{4}+\frac{3}{4}\times\frac{2}{3}=$ $-\frac{3}{4}+\frac{1}{2}=$ $-\frac{3}{4}+\frac{2}{4}=\left(-\frac{1}{4}\right)$

b. $\left(\frac{3}{8}\right)\left(-\frac{4}{5}\right)\div\frac{1}{2}=$ $-\frac{3}{10}\div\frac{1}{2}=$ $-\frac{3}{10}\times\frac{2}{1}=\frac{-6}{10}=\left(\frac{-3}{5}\right)$

c. $\left(\frac{2}{3}\right)^2\times\frac{1}{4}=$ $\frac{4}{9}\times\frac{1}{4}=\left(\frac{1}{9}\right)$

2.) $12.6\div3=(4.2)$
$(4.2+4.2+4.2=12.6)$

3.) 100 cm. = 1 m.
1,000 m = 1 km
$300{,}000\text{ cm}\cdot\frac{1}{100\text{ cm}}=\frac{300{,}000\text{ m}}{100}=(3{,}000\text{ m})$
$3{,}000\text{ m}\cdot\frac{1\text{ km}}{1{,}000\text{ m}}=\frac{3{,}000\text{ km}}{1{,}000}=(3\text{ km})$

4.) a. $\frac{2}{5}\div\frac{4}{5}=\frac{2}{5}\times\frac{5}{4}=\left(\frac{1}{2}\right)$

b. $2\frac{1}{3}=2\frac{2}{6}=1\frac{8}{6}$
$-1\frac{1}{2}=1\frac{3}{6}=1\frac{3}{6}$
$\left(\frac{5}{6}\right)$

5.) (97)

6.) $10^{-3}=(.001)$ $10^{-2}=(.01)$ $10^{-1}=(.1)$ $10^0=(1)$
$10^1=(10)$ $10^2=(100)$ $10^3=(1{,}000)$
$10^4=(10{,}000)$ $10^5=(100{,}000)$ $10^6=(1{,}000{,}000)$

7.) $m=\frac{8-3}{3-1}$ $\left(\frac{5}{2}\right)$

8.) a. $(2n>n+8)$ b. $(.42n=168)$ c. $(n-5<2)$

9.) a. $3x=\frac{1}{3}$
$\frac{1}{3}\cdot3x=\frac{1}{3}\cdot\frac{1}{3}$
$\left(x=\frac{1}{9}\right)$

b. $\frac{3}{4}x=15$
$\frac{4}{3}\cdot\frac{3}{4}x=15\cdot\frac{4}{3}$
$(x=20)$

c. $-\frac{1}{2}x=-3.2$
$-2\cdot-\frac{1}{2}x=-3.2\cdot-2$
$(x=6.4)$

10.) $7\frac{1}{2}\div2\frac{1}{4}=$
$\frac{15}{2}\div\frac{9}{4}=$
$\frac{15}{2}\times\frac{4}{9}=\frac{10}{3}=3\frac{1}{3}$
(3 rests)

11.) a. 10 → (2)(5) b. 15 → (3)(5) c. 25 → (5)(5)
d. $2\times3\times5\times5=(150)$

1.) a. $400\overline{)8934.000}$ = 22.335 ≈ (22.34 or $22\frac{67}{200}$)
800
934
−800
1340
−1200
1400
−1200
2000

b. $.03\overline{)9.012}$ = (300.4)

2.) a. $.32\times100=(32)$
b. $54{,}793.6\div1{,}000=(54.7936)$
c. $.578629\times10{,}000=(5{,}786.29)$

3.) (Four hundred eighty-three thousand five hundred fifty-two.)

4.) $\frac{25}{40}=\frac{60}{x}$
$25x=2400$
$x=(96\text{ cm})$

5.) a. (3.17 3.13 3.13 3.14)
b. $\frac{3.17+3.13+3.13+3.14}{4}\approx(3.14)$
c. (circumference to diameter)

6.) $8=7\frac{8}{8}$
$-4\frac{3}{8}=-4\frac{3}{8}$
$\left(3\frac{5}{8}\right)$

7.) ⊙ C containing D
⊙ D containing C
⊙ C ∩ ⊙ D at E and F
$\overline{EF}\perp\overline{CD}$ and
$\overline{EF}$ bisects $\overline{CD}$

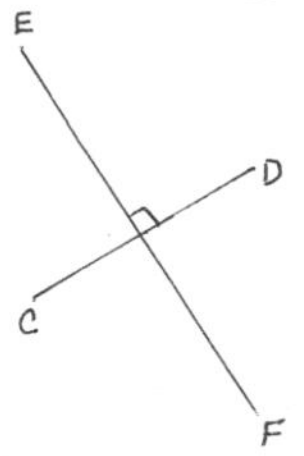

8.) $28\div7=4$
$35\div7=5$ (C)
$56\div7=8$

9.) $3\frac{1}{2}\div\frac{3}{8}$
$\frac{7}{2}\times\frac{8}{3}=\frac{28}{3}=9\frac{1}{3}$
(9 scarves)

10.) $\frac{\$360}{\$4000}$ $4{,}000\overline{)360.00}$ = .09
360.00
(9%)

11.) Put in decimal form
.3, −33$\overline{3}$, .33, .303, .334
(.300 .303 .33 $33\frac{1}{3}$% .334)

1.) a. $\frac{8}{24}=\left(\frac{1}{3}\right)$ b. $\frac{9}{24}=\left(\frac{3}{8}\right)$ c. $\frac{10}{24}=\left(\frac{5}{12}\right)$

2.) a. $\frac{1}{9}\times\frac{3}{10}=\left(\frac{1}{30}\right)$
b. $\frac{1}{9}\div\frac{1}{3}=\frac{1}{9}\times\frac{3}{1}=\left(\frac{1}{3}\right)$

3.) $1^2=(1)$ $2^2=(4)$ $3^2=(9)$ $4^2=(16)$
$5^2=(25)$ $6^2=(36)$ $7^2=(49)$ $8^2=(64)$
$9^2=(81)$ $10^2=(100)$ $11^2=(121)$ $12^2=(144)$

4.) a. $p=8+3.2+4+4.2=(19.4\text{ cm})$
b. $A=\frac{1}{2}\times3(8+4)$
$\frac{1}{2}\times3\times12=(18\text{ cm}^2)$

5.) a. $2x-3=-9$
$+3\quad+3$
$2x=-6$
$\frac{1}{2}\cdot2x=-6\cdot\frac{1}{2}$
$(x=-3)$

b. $\frac{1}{2}x+\frac{2}{3}=\frac{5}{6}=\frac{5}{6}$
$-\frac{2}{3}\quad-\frac{2}{3}=-\frac{4}{6}$
$\frac{1}{2}x=\frac{1}{6}$
$2\cdot\frac{1}{2}x=\frac{1}{6}\cdot2$
$\left(x=\frac{1}{3}\right)$

c. $-x+3=-2$
$-3\quad-3$
$-x=-5$
$(x=5)$

6.) 5·4·3·2·1
(120 different ways)

7.) a. (27) b. (58) c. (100)
d. (42) e. (83) f. (6)

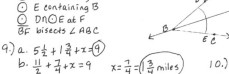

8.) ⊙ B intersect $\overline{AB}$ and $\overline{BC}$ at D and E
⊙ D containing B
⊙ E containing B
⊙ D ∩ ⊙ E at F
$\overline{BF}$ bisects ∠ABC

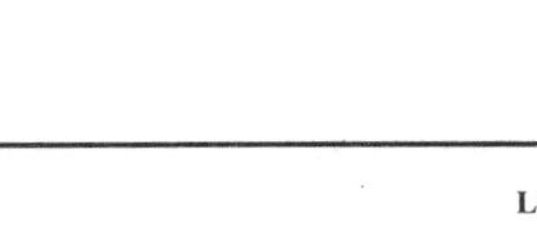

9.) a. $5\frac{1}{2}+1\frac{3}{4}+x=(9)$
b. $\frac{11}{2}+\frac{7}{4}+x=9$
$\frac{22}{4}+\frac{7}{4}+x=9$
$\frac{29}{4}+x=9=\frac{36}{4}$
$-\frac{29}{4}\qquad-\frac{29}{4}$
$\frac{7}{4}$
$x=\frac{7}{4}=\left(1\frac{3}{4}\text{ miles}\right)$

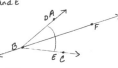

10.) a. $(2n-5)$
b. $(-n)$
c. (n^3-5)

1.) $3\times3=9$
$9\times3=27$
$27\times3=81$
$81\times3=(243)$

2.) a. (5) b. (6) c. $\left(\frac{1}{2}\right)$ d. $\left(\frac{5}{6}\right)$
e. ($\sqrt{25}$ and $\sqrt{36}$, 5 and 6)

3.) a. 24 allowable letters. Duplicates allowed.
$24\times24=(576\text{ ways})$
b. 10 digits (0 through 10) $24\times24\times10=(5{,}760\text{ ways})$

4.) a. $\frac{2.28}{3}=\left(\frac{\$.76}{\text{pound}}\right)$
b. $10\times.76=(\$7.60)$

5.) $800{,}000-300{,}000=(500{,}000)$

6.) a. (pyramid or square pyramid)
b. (cylinder)
c. (prism or triangular prism)

7.) $V=\frac{4}{3}(3.14)(7)^3=$
(1436.03 in^3)

8.) a. (x^4) b. (3^5)
c. $(2xy^2)$ d. $\left(\left(\frac{1}{2}\right)^4\right)$

9.) $\frac{6{,}000{,}000}{1{,}000}$ 6,000 (C)

10.) $5\text{ hrs}\cdot\frac{60\text{ min.}}{1\text{ hr.}}\cdot\frac{1\text{ program}}{12\text{ min.}}=\frac{5\cdot60}{12}$ programs $=(25\text{ programs})$

11. Answers will vary

1.) a. $3a + 2b + 8a$ = $11a + 2b$ b. $3x^2 - x^2 + x + 1$ = $2x^2 + x + 1$

2.) $.82 \overline{)\,.6724}$ = .82
−656
164
−164

3.) 821,000,000

4.) $\frac{\$1.49}{18.8}$ = \$.08 ounce

5.) $15 = p \cdot 75$
$\frac{15}{75} = p$
$.2 = p$ (20%)

6.) use the problem solving strategy of trial and error.
Linda, Cheryl, Carolyn, Kathy

7.) a. $(8-3)^2 - 4 \times 2 =$
$5^2 - 4 \times 2$
$25 - 4 \times 2$
$25 - 8 = 17$

b. $20 \div 2 \times 2^2 =$
$20 \div 2 \times 4$
$10 \times 4 = 40$

c. $3 - (-8) =$
$3 + 8 = 11$

8.) a. 323 x 100 (move decimal 2 places to the right) 32,300
b. 63,600 ÷ 100 (move decimal 2 places to the left) 636.00 (636)

9.) (1,−3) (5,17) $\frac{17-(-3)}{5-1} = \frac{20}{4} = 5$
constant difference is 5
$-3 + 5 = 2 + 5 = 7$

10.) $.041 = \frac{41}{1000}$, $.014 = \frac{14}{1000}$
$.004 = \frac{4}{1000}$, $.001 = \frac{1}{1000}$
.001 .004 .014 .041

11.) Monday = \$10 Tuesday = $\frac{1}{2}(10)$ = \$5 Wednesday = $\frac{1}{5}(10)$ = \$2
\$10 + \$5 + \$2 = \$17.00

12.) a. $|-6| = 6$ b. $|-16| = 16$ c. $|-25| = 25$

1.) (a.) 20% x 1,000 = 200
b. century and a half = 100 + 50 = 150

2.) a. $\frac{2}{5} \times \frac{7}{3} = \frac{14}{5} = 2\frac{4}{5}$
b. $2\frac{1}{6} \div 3\frac{1}{3} = \frac{13}{6} \div \frac{10}{3}$
$\frac{13}{6} \times \frac{3}{10} = \frac{13}{20}$

3.) a. 3 b. 2 c. 4th d. 8

4.) $18 \overline{)\,1234}$ = $68\frac{10}{18}$
−108
154
−144
10
$68\frac{5}{9}$ or 68.56

5.) a. $\frac{1}{4}$ = .25 = 25%
b. $\frac{1}{4}$
c. .25 x 2000 = 500 with blue hue

6.) a. 10% (yellow) x 4 = 40% (blue) (a. blue than yellow)
b. 0% (green) x $\frac{2}{3}$ = 20% (red) (b. red as green)

7.) $\frac{1}{160} = \frac{4.5}{x}$
x = 720 in.
720 in. x $\frac{1 \text{ ft.}}{12 \text{ in.}}$ = 60 ft.

8.) a.

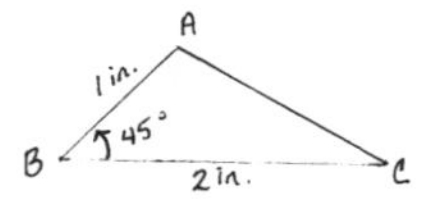

b. If two sides and the included angle of one triangle are congruent to two sides and the included angle of another, the triangles are congruent. or SAS congruence.

9.) a. m = 0 1 2 3 4 5 6
b = 140 130 120 110 100 90 80
b. b = 140 − 10m
c. b = 140 − 10(11)
140 − 110 = \$30

10.) a.

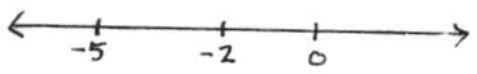

b. T

1.) a. $10\frac{1}{6} = 10\frac{1}{6} = 9\frac{7}{6}$
$-8\frac{1}{2} = -8\frac{3}{6} = -8\frac{3}{6}$
$1\frac{4}{6} = 1\frac{2}{3}$

b. $3\frac{3}{4} \div 1\frac{2}{3} =$
$\frac{15}{4} \div \frac{5}{3} =$
$\frac{15}{4} \times \frac{3}{5} = \frac{9}{4} = 2\frac{1}{4}$

2.) a.

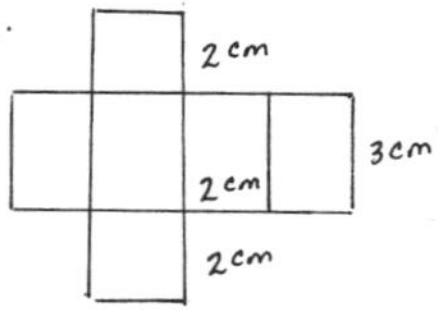

b. SA = 8x3 + 2(2x2) =
24 + 8 = 32 cm²
c. V = 4x3 = 12 cm³

3.) $33 \overline{)\,\$329.01}$ = \$9.97
−297
320
−297
231
−231

4.) $\frac{2}{5} = \frac{7}{x}$
35 = 2x
17.5 = x
x = 17.5 in.

5.) a. 2x + 4y − 2y + x
3x + 2y
b. 2x − 3(x+4)
2x − 3x − 12
−x − 12

6.) a.

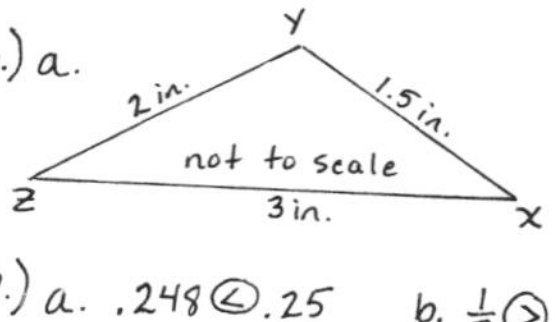

b. If three sides of a triangle are congruent to three sides of another triangle, then the triangles will be congruent. or SSS congruence.

7.) a. .248 < .25
.248 .250
b. $\frac{1}{3}$ > .3
.333 .300
c. −1.3 < −1.2
d. $\frac{4}{5}$ > $\frac{3}{4}$

8) 8:50
+ 2:30
11:20 New York time
11:20 New York time
− 3:00 time difference
8:20 LA time
8:20pm.

9.) answers will vary

1.) a. $8\frac{1}{2} = 8.5$
$51 \overline{)\,8.500}$ = $.1\overline{6} = \frac{1}{6}$
−51
340
−306
340
−306
34
$8\frac{1}{2} \div \frac{1}{6} = 51$
b. $\frac{1}{2} \times \frac{1}{4} = \frac{1}{8}$

2.) a. 5 b. 50 c. 500 d. 5,000 e. 50,000 f. 500,000
g. 5,000,000 h. 50,000,000 5x10ⁿ is 5 followed by n zeros

3.) 2.03 x .023 = .04669 − multiply the two numbers then move the decimal 5 places to the left.

4.) \$3.50 (per box) x .3 (profit) =
\$1.05 x 250 (boxes sold) =
\$262.50

5.) move decimal 4 places to the right.
4.37628 = 4,376.28

6.) a. $\frac{1^2 - 1^{10}}{1^{12}}$
$\frac{1-1}{1} = 0$

b. $4 + 3(5-2)^2$
$4 + 3(3)^2$
$4 + 3 \times 9$
$4 + 27 = 31$

c. $4\left(\frac{3}{4}\right)^2 =$
$4\left(\frac{9}{16}\right) = \frac{9}{4} = 2\frac{1}{4}$

7)

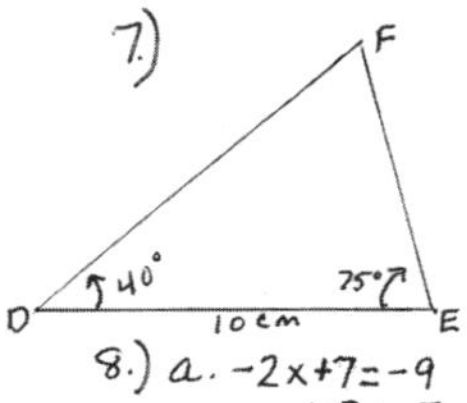

when two angles and the included side of one triangle are congruent to the two angles and the included side of another, the triangles are congruent, or ASA congruence.

8.) a. −2x + 7 = −9
−7 −7
−2x = −16
$-\frac{1}{2} \cdot -2x = -16 \cdot -\frac{1}{2}$
x = 8

b. $\frac{1}{5}x = 4$
$5 \cdot \frac{1}{5}x = 4 \cdot 5$
x = 20

9.) $3\frac{3}{4} \div \frac{3}{4} = \frac{15}{4} \div \frac{3}{4}$
$\frac{15}{4} \times \frac{4}{3}$ = 5 portions
He has 4 siblings

10.) a. $\frac{5}{6} = \frac{5}{6}$
$-\frac{1}{2} = \frac{3}{6}$
$\frac{2}{6} = \frac{1}{3}$

1.) a. (30) b. (7,200)

2.) a. $8\frac{5}{6} = 8\frac{5}{6}$; $-3\frac{1}{2} = 3\frac{3}{6}$; $5\frac{2}{6} = (5\frac{1}{3})$

b. $5\frac{1}{8} = 4\frac{9}{8}$; $-2\frac{3}{4} = -2\frac{6}{8}$; $(2\frac{3}{8})$

3.) a. $\frac{2}{3} \neq \frac{66}{100}$; $198 \neq 200$

b. $\frac{4}{9} \neq \frac{8}{20}$; $72 \neq 80$

(c.) $\frac{4}{5} = \frac{44}{55}$; 220 = 220 T

4.) a. $\frac{21}{10} \times \frac{13}{5} = \frac{273}{50} = (5\frac{23}{50})$

b. $\frac{2}{3} \div \frac{2}{5}$; $\frac{2}{3} \times \frac{5}{2} = \frac{5}{3} = (1\frac{2}{3})$

5.) 37% of \$1.00 = \$.37
\$.25 + .10 + .01 + .01 = \$.37
(quarter) (dime) (penny) (penny)
(4 coins)

6.) $\frac{5}{3} = \frac{x}{9}$
$3x = 45$
$\frac{1}{3} \cdot 3x = 45 \cdot \frac{1}{3}$
(x = 15 runs)

7.) 93,000,000 (9.3×10^7)

8.) a. (7+8)
b. (4+5+6)
c. (1+2+3+4+5)

9.) Factors of:
16 = 1, 2, (4), 8, 16
20 = 1, 2, (4), 5, 10, 20
24 = 1, 2, 3, (4), 6, 8, 12, 24
(GCF = 4)

10.) $\frac{6}{9} \times \left(\frac{3}{3}\right) = \frac{(18)}{27} \div \left(\frac{9}{9}\right) =$
$\frac{2}{(3)} \times \left(\frac{12}{12}\right) = \frac{24}{(36)}$

11.) $\frac{7 \text{ games won}}{10 \text{ total games}} = \frac{70}{100} = (70\%)$

12.) 2,000.7
+ .83
(2,001.53)

1.) a. $21\overline{)1984}$ = (94 r 10)
189
94
−84
10

b. $.009\overline{).081}$ = (9.)

2.) a. (n+6−5)
b. (n^2+6)
c. (−n+−5)

3.) change to decimals:
$\frac{14}{15} = .933$ $\frac{4}{5} = .8$ $\frac{19}{20} = .95$
$\frac{9}{10} = .9$ so $\left(\frac{4}{5} < \frac{9}{10} < \frac{14}{15} < \frac{19}{20}\right)$

4.) a. $\frac{\frac{1}{4}}{\frac{3}{4}}$; $\frac{1}{4} \div \frac{3}{4}$; $\frac{1}{4} \times \frac{4}{3} = (\frac{1}{3})$

b. $\frac{1}{3} = \frac{x}{12}$
$3x = 12$
$\frac{1}{3} \cdot 3x = 12 \cdot \frac{1}{3}$
(x = 4 cups)

c. $4\frac{1}{3} \div \frac{1}{4}$ How many $\frac{1}{4}$ cups in $4\frac{1}{3}$
$\frac{13}{3} \cdot 4 = \frac{52}{3} =$ (17 smoothies)

5.) 8" x 10" base becomes 6x8 = 48 in²
V = 48 x 1 = (48 in³)

6.) a. m∠A = m∠X (T)
b. BC = xy (F)
c. $\overline{AB} \cong \overline{xy}$ (T)
d. ∠C ≅ ∠2 (T)

7.) a. (8,4)
b. $\frac{32}{64} = (\frac{1}{2})$
c. (1)

8.) a. 40,000,000 (4.0×10^7)
b. 3,000,000,000,000 = (3.0×10^{12})

9.) (2a + 15 = 24)

10.) 100% − 15% = 85%
.85 x 159 = (\$135.15)
discounted price

100% + 6% = 106% cost w/ tax
1.06 x \$135.15 = \$143.259 or
(\$143.26) you have enough money

11.) $\sqrt{\frac{36}{49}} = (\frac{6}{7})$

1.) a $7 \div \frac{2}{3} =$
$7 \div \frac{3}{2} = \frac{21}{2} = (10\frac{1}{2})$

b. $2\frac{4}{5} \times \frac{1}{7} =$
$\frac{14}{5} \times \frac{1}{7} = (\frac{2}{5})$

2.) a. (geometric)
b. (48, 96)

3.) (.0624)

4.) a. $x^2 = 16$
($x = \pm 4$)
b. |x| = 8
($x = \pm 8$)
c. $\sqrt{x} = 5$
(x = 25)

5.) a. d = 65.4 (260 mi)
b. $t = \frac{628}{70} \approx 8.97$ (about 9 hrs.)
c. d = (55x)

6.) \$13.20
10% of 13.20 = 1.32
5% is $\frac{1}{2}$ x 1.32 = + .66
1.98
Dinner tip
\$13.20 + \$1.98 = (\$15.18)

7.) a. $\frac{3}{5}$ = water + $(\frac{2}{5})$ = land
b. $\frac{2}{5} = (40\%)$; $5\overline{)2.00}$ = .40; −20; 00

8.) a. $-8(5-3)^2 - 2 =$
$-8(2)^2 - 2 =$
$-8 \cdot 4 - 2 =$
$-32 - 2 = (-34)$

b. $\frac{4-2}{4} = \frac{2}{4} = (\frac{1}{2})$

9.) a. x − y = 2
((4,2) (2,0) (0,−2))
b.

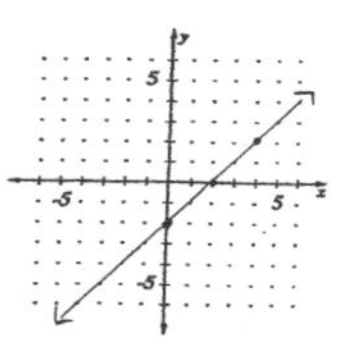

c. $m = \frac{0-2}{2-4} = \frac{-2}{-2} = (1)$

10.) \$1.25 x 7 = \$8.75
\$1.35 x 8 = \$10.80
.65 x 9 = 5.85
.50 x 15 = 7.50
(\$32.90)

1.) a. (−2)(−2)(2) (>) (−2)(2)(2)
8 −8

b. 1.0×10^4 (>) 1,000
10,000 1,000

c. $\frac{1}{4} \times \frac{1}{4}$ (<) $\frac{1}{4} \div \frac{1}{4}$
$\frac{1}{16}$ $\frac{1}{4} \times \frac{4}{1} = 1$

d. 10^2 (<) 2^{10}
100 1,024

2.) $F = \frac{9}{5}(45) + 32$
= 81 + 32 = (113°F)

3.) a. \$2.85 + \$4.50 + \$1.15 =
\$2.85 + \$1.15 + \$4.50 = (\$8.50)

b. $\frac{2}{5} + \frac{1}{3} + \frac{3}{5} + \frac{2}{3} =$
$\frac{2}{5} + \frac{3}{5} + \frac{1}{3} + \frac{2}{3} = (2)$

4.) (4)

5.) a. $\frac{1}{4} \times \frac{3}{5} = (\frac{3}{20})$
b. $2\frac{1}{3} \div \frac{1}{6} = \frac{7}{3} \div \frac{1}{6}$
$\frac{7}{3} \times \frac{6}{1} = (14)$

6.) (four hundred twenty-nine ten thousandths)

7.) a. (32, −64)
b. $(r = \frac{8}{-4} = -2)$
c. (multiply the previous term times −2)

8.) (a) = 12 x 12 = (144)
b = 12 x 12 x 12 = 1,728
(c) = (144) (12 x 12)
(d) = 720 ÷ 5 = (144)

9.) (yards, miles, meters, kilometers)

10.) a. .10
−.01
(.09)

b. .010
−.001
(.009)

11.) \$1.59 price
−.50 discount
\$1.09 discounted price
\$1.09
x 6 bottles
(\$6.54)

12.) a. perimeter (ΔDEF) = perimeter (ΔGHI) (T)
b. m∠E = m∠H (T)
c. $\overline{DE} \cong \overline{HI}$ (F)

1.) a. $4\frac{1}{8} = 3\frac{9}{8}$
$-3\frac{3}{4} = 3\frac{6}{8}$
$\boxed{\frac{3}{8}}$

b. $\frac{1}{2} + \frac{1}{4} + \frac{1}{8} =$
$\frac{4}{8} + \frac{2}{8} + \frac{1}{8} = \boxed{\frac{7}{8}}$

2.) $8.97 - 3.09 \approx$
$9 - 3 \approx \boxed{6}$

3.) a. $100\% - 20\% = 80\%$
$.8p = 28.80$

b. $\frac{.8}{.8}p = \frac{28.80}{.8}$
$p = \boxed{\$36}$

4.) $\frac{2}{3} = \boxed{\frac{4}{6} = \frac{8}{12} = \frac{16}{24}}$

5.) a. $1\frac{3}{5} \div \frac{3}{5} = \frac{8}{5} \div \frac{3}{5}$
$\frac{8}{5} \times \frac{5}{3} = \frac{8}{3} = \boxed{2\frac{2}{3}}$

b. $7\frac{1}{2} \times 3\frac{3}{5} = \frac{15}{2} \times \frac{18}{5} = \boxed{27}$

6.) a. $V = S^3$ $V = 1^3 = \boxed{1 \text{ in.}^3}$
b. $S = 2$ $V = 2^3 = \boxed{8 \text{ in.}^3}$
c. $\boxed{8 \text{ times}}$

7.) a. $-3x - 7 = \boxed{21}$ b. $\left(-\frac{2}{3}\right)\left(-\frac{9}{10}\right) = \boxed{\frac{3}{5}}$ c. $-100 \times 40 = \boxed{4{,}000}$ d. positive

8.) $\boxed{25, 36, 49}$ 9.) $8{,}000 \div 100 = \boxed{80}$

10.) a. $|4| \ \textcircled{=}\ |-4|$ (4, 4) b. $4^2 \ \textcircled{=}\ (-4)^2$ (16, 16) c. $2^4 \ \textcircled{=}\ 4^2$ (16, 16) d. $4^1 \ \textcircled{=}\ 4 \times 10^0$ (4, 4)

11.) 90% = decrease past 60 yrs.
10% = remaining
10% of 300,000

$300{,}000 \times .10 = \boxed{30{,}000}$

12.) $81{,}000 + 7{,}000 + 10{,}000 + 3{,}000 = 101{,}000$ $\boxed{b}$

1.) a. $18\frac{1}{3} = 18\frac{2}{6} = 17\frac{8}{6}$
$-7\frac{5}{6} = -7\frac{5}{6} = -7\frac{5}{6}$
$10\frac{3}{6} = \boxed{10\frac{1}{2}}$

b. $14\frac{1}{10} = 14\frac{2}{20} = 13\frac{22}{20}$
$-2\frac{3}{4} = -2\frac{15}{20} = -2\frac{15}{20}$
$\boxed{11\frac{7}{20}}$

2.) a. $\frac{12}{100} = \boxed{12\%}$
b. $\frac{12}{50} \times \left(\frac{2}{2}\right) = \frac{24}{100} = \boxed{24\%}$ or $12.00 \div 50 = .24 = 24\%$ (-100, 200)
c. $\frac{12}{25} \times \left(\frac{4}{4}\right) = \frac{48}{100} = \boxed{48\%}$ or $12.00 \div 25 = .48 = 48\%$ (-100, 200)

3.) Change to decimals:
$\frac{47}{5} = 9.4$ $\frac{56}{6} = 9.33$ $\frac{64}{7} = 9.142$
$\frac{78}{8} = 9.75$ $\boxed{\frac{64}{7}\ \frac{56}{6}\ \frac{47}{5}\ \frac{78}{8}}$

4.) 2 million $\frac{\text{blood cells}}{\text{sec}} \cdot \frac{60 \text{ sec.}}{1 \text{ min.}} =$
$2{,}000{,}000 \times 60 =$
$\boxed{120{,}000{,}000 \frac{\text{blood cells}}{\text{min.}}}$

5.) $394 \div 72 = 5\frac{34}{72}$ (-360, 34) or $\boxed{5\frac{17}{36} \text{ or } 5.47}$

6.) $1^3 = \boxed{1}$ $2^3 = \boxed{8}$ $3^3 = \boxed{27}$
$4^3 = \boxed{64}$ $5^3 = \boxed{125}$

7.) $\frac{64}{8} = 8$ $8n = 24$
$24 \div 8 = 3$ $\boxed{n = 3}$

8.) $\frac{72}{\textcircled{2}} = 36$ $\frac{72}{\textcircled{3}} = 24$ $\frac{72}{\textcircled{4}} = 18$
$\frac{72}{\textcircled{6}} = 12$ $\frac{72}{\textcircled{8}} = 9$ $\frac{72}{\textcircled{9}} = 8$

9.) $A = \frac{1}{2}bh$ $b = 6 \text{in}$ $h = 8 \text{in}$
$A = \frac{1}{2}(8 \times 6) = A = \frac{1}{2} \times \frac{48}{1}$
$\boxed{A = 24 \text{ sq in.}}$

10.) a. $\frac{2}{5} \times \frac{3}{10} = \boxed{\frac{3}{25}}$
b. $5\frac{2}{3} \div 2\frac{1}{4} = \frac{17}{3} \div \frac{9}{4}$
$\frac{17}{3} \times \frac{4}{9} = \frac{68}{27} = \boxed{2\frac{14}{27}}$

11.) $\frac{2}{6} = \frac{17}{18}$
$\frac{2}{6} \times \left(\frac{3}{8}\right) = \frac{\textcircled{6}}{18}$

12.) a. $\frac{2500}{720} = \frac{250}{72} = \frac{125}{36} \approx \boxed{3.5 \frac{\text{books}}{\text{student}}}$
b. (No. They needed to read 4 books each.)

1.) a. $6\frac{3}{4} \div 3\frac{3}{4} =$
$\frac{27}{4} \div \frac{15}{4} =$
$\frac{27}{4} \times \frac{4}{15} = \frac{9}{5} = \boxed{1\frac{4}{5}}$

b. $1\frac{3}{5} \div 5 =$
$\frac{8}{5} \div 5 =$
$\frac{8}{5} \times \frac{1}{5} = \boxed{\frac{8}{25}}$

2.) a. $5.11 \times 6.98 \approx 5 \times 7 \approx \boxed{35}$
b. $4.9 - 5.3 + 7.2 \approx$
$5 - 5 + 7 \approx \boxed{7}$

3.) a.

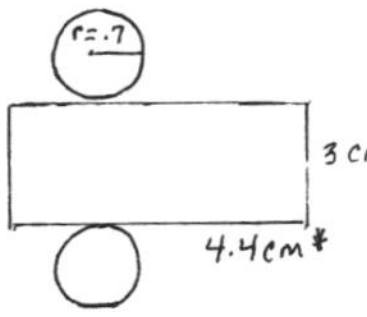

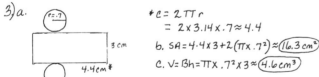

* $C = 2\pi r$
$= 2 \times 3.14 \times .7 \approx 4.4$
b. $SA = 4.4 \times 3 + 2(\pi \times .7^2) \approx \boxed{16.3 \text{ cm}^2}$
c. $V = Bh = \pi \times .7^2 \times 3 \approx \boxed{4.6 \text{ cm}^3}$

4.) $10 \times 2 = \boxed{2 \text{ hours}}$

5.) $478.56 \div 4.8 = \boxed{99.7}$
-432
465
-432
336
-336

6.) $2 + 5 + 0 + (-3) = \boxed{4 \text{ over par}}$

7.) a. 6,000 b. $\boxed{500{,}000}$
c. $\boxed{180{,}000}$ d. $\boxed{100{,}000{,}000}$

8.) $4{,}700 - 699 = \boxed{4{,}001}$

9.) a. 12 in. = 1 ft. 3 ft. = 1 yd.
$468 \text{ in.} \cdot \frac{1 \text{ ft.}}{12 \text{ in.}} = \boxed{39 \text{ ft.}} \cdot \frac{1 \text{ yd}}{3 \text{ ft.}} = \boxed{13 \text{ yds}}$
b. 10 mm = 1 cm 100 cm = 1 m
$59{,}000 \text{ mm} \cdot \frac{1 \text{ cm}}{10 \text{ mm}} = \boxed{5{,}900 \text{ cm}} \cdot \frac{1 \text{ m}}{100 \text{ cm}}$
$\boxed{59 \text{ m}}$

10.) a. $\frac{3}{10} \times \frac{1}{2} = \boxed{\frac{3}{20}}$
b. $\frac{10}{1} \div \frac{1}{5}$ $\frac{10}{1} \times \frac{5}{1} = \boxed{50}$

11.) a. This graph makes it look like there is a larger difference than there really is.
b. Central is much more favorable in the redrawn graph. They would prefer it.

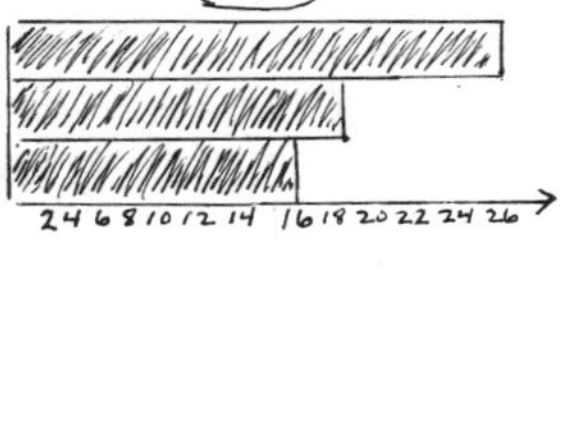

1.) a. $\frac{1}{3} \times 4\frac{1}{5} =$
$\frac{1}{3} \times \frac{21}{5} = \frac{7}{5} = \boxed{1\frac{2}{5}}$

b. $\frac{1}{4} \times \frac{3}{8} = \boxed{\frac{3}{32}}$

2.) a. $\frac{3}{9} = \frac{1}{3} = .33\bar{3}$ $\frac{1}{3} = .33\bar{3}$
b. $\textcircled{\frac{4}{9}} = .44\bar{4}$ $\frac{1}{2} = .50$
c. $\frac{6}{9} = \frac{2}{3} = .66\bar{6}$

3.)
b height of a basketball player
d distance from Chicago to Detroit
a diameter of a dime
c diagonal of a computer screen

4.) $2 + n + n = 8$
$2 + 2n = 8$
$+{-2}$ $+{-2}$
$2n = 6$
$\frac{1}{2} \cdot 2n = 6 \cdot \frac{1}{2}$ $\boxed{n = 3}$

5.) a.

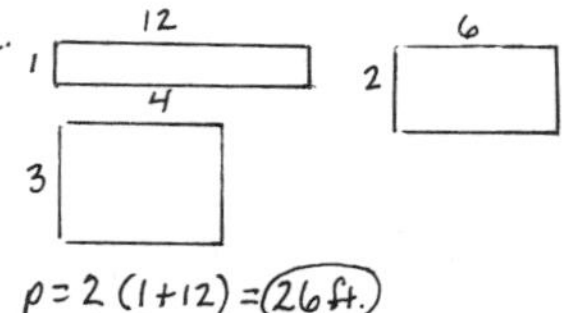

6.) a. $600 \div 10 = \boxed{60}$
b. $9{,}000 \div 30 = \boxed{300}$
c. $1000{,}00 \div 100 = \boxed{10{,}000}$

b. $p = 2(1 + 12) = \boxed{26 \text{ ft.}}$
$p = 2(2 + 6) = \boxed{16 \text{ ft.}}$
$p = 2(3 + 4) = \boxed{14 \text{ ft.}}$
c. The 3x4 = the smallest perimeter

7.) $3 \times 6 \times 2 = \boxed{36}$ different outfits

8.) 1 l = 1,000 ml, so 1 liter weighs $\boxed{1{,}000 \text{g.}}$

9.) a. $|-2| = \boxed{2}$
b. $(-2)^2 = \boxed{4}$
c. $(-(-2))^2 = 2^2 = \boxed{4}$

10.) $5.5\% = .055$
$.055 \times 1{,}800{,}000 =$
$\boxed{\$99{,}000}$

11.) C = change in temp.
$-7° + C = 11°$
$\boxed{C = 18°F}$

12.) a. $\boxed{35}$ b. $\boxed{\frac{1}{3} = .3\bar{3}}$
c. $\boxed{\frac{70}{200} = .35}$ d. $\boxed{.35}$

1.) $\frac{3}{4} = 75\%$ $\frac{x}{12} = 75\%$
$x = 12 \times .75$ ($x = 9$)

2.) a. $3x + 6 = -9$
$+-6 \quad +-6$
$3x = -15$
$\frac{1}{3} \cdot 3x = -15 \cdot \frac{1}{3}$
($x = -5$)

b. $\frac{2}{3}x = \frac{5}{9}$
$\frac{3}{2} \cdot \frac{2}{3}x = \frac{5}{9} \cdot \frac{3}{2}$
($x = \frac{5}{6}$)

c. $-2x = -5$
$-\frac{1}{2} \cdot -2x = -5 \cdot -\frac{1}{2}$ ($x = \frac{5}{2} = 2\frac{1}{2}$)

3) b. (46 milliliters)

4.) (8, 20)

5.) a. $\frac{65 + 79 + 92 + 100 + 100}{5} = \frac{436}{5} = (87.2)$

b. 65 79 [92] 100 100 c. (The median score suggests an A-)

6.) a. d=rt $\frac{312}{60} = t \approx$ (5 hrs)

b. $\frac{mi.}{gal.}$ $\frac{312}{30} \approx$ (10 gallons)

7.) 7,000 − 200 = (6,800)

8.) a. (9)
b. (6,100)
c. (7,200)

9.) a. 9.45
x 3.2
1890
2835
(30.240)

b. .083
x.02
.00166
(.00166)

10.) 100% + 15% = 115% 115% = 1.15
1.15 x 45 = (51.75)

11.) (the amount of the paycheck)

12.) (31, 17, 3)

1.) $20\% = \frac{20}{100} = (\frac{1}{5}) = (.20)$
$(10\%) = \frac{10}{100} = \frac{1}{10} = (.10)$
$80\% = \frac{80}{100} = \frac{8}{10} = (\frac{4}{5}) = (.80)$
$(33\frac{1}{3}\%) = \frac{333}{1000} = (\frac{1}{3}) = .33\bar{3}$

2.) a. $3x^2 - x + 2x^2 - x$
($5x^2 - 2x$)
b. $4x^2 - 5(x^2 - x)$
$4x^2 - 5x^2 + 5x$
($-x^2 + 5x$)

3.) 19+1, 18+2, 17+3, 16+4, 15+5, 14+6, 13+7, 14−6=8
so (14 and 6)

4.) (5n + 3 = 15)

5.) $\frac{mi}{gal}$ $\frac{392}{14}$ = ($\frac{28\ mi}{gal.}$)

6.) $\frac{73}{150} = .48\bar{6}$ or (.487)

7.) a. $\sqrt{9}$ = (3) b. $\sqrt{49}$ = (7)
c. $\sqrt{\frac{1}{36}}$ = ($\frac{1}{6}$) d. $\sqrt{.01}$ = (.1)

8.) a. x + y = 4
((0,4) (4,0) (2,2))
c. y = 3x
((0,0) (1,3) (−1,−3))
e. ((1,3))

b.+d.

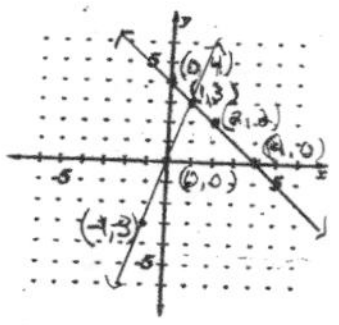

9.) $\sqrt{\frac{9}{25}} = \frac{3}{5} = .6$ $\frac{2}{3} = .\bar{6}$ 62% = .62 .66
.60 .66 .62 .66
($\sqrt{\frac{9}{25}}$, 62%, .66, $\frac{2}{3}$)

10.) a. (z) b. (y) c. (x)

11.) 120% x 100
1.2 x 100 =
(120)

1.) (c) 5.5 meters

2.) a. 10.040
−.684
(9.356)

b. 5.400
−.003
(5.397)

3.) a. 37.68 ÷ 100 = (37.68) b. 24.99 ÷ 100 = (.7499)
c. 00.2 ÷ 100 = (.002) d. 5600.00 ÷ 100 = (5,600)

4.) (16) (24) (32) (48)

5.) a x = −2 −1 0 1 2
y = (4 1 0 1 4)

b.

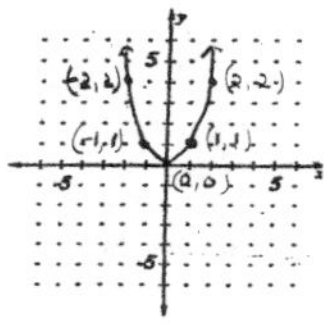

6.) $60 \div 6\frac{1}{4} =$
$60 \div \frac{25}{4} =$
$60 \times \frac{4}{25} = \frac{48}{5} = 9.6$
(9 frames)

7.) $\frac{3}{8} \div \frac{3}{4} =$
$\frac{3}{8} \times \frac{4}{3} = (\frac{1}{2}\ mi)$

8.) a. $A = 5^2$
$\frac{1}{9} = 5^2$
$\frac{1}{3} = 5$ ($\frac{1}{3}$ ft.)
b. $p = 4(\frac{1}{3}) =$ ($\frac{4}{3}$ or $1\frac{1}{3}$ ft.)

9.) a. $4 = 3\frac{6}{6}$
$-3\frac{5}{6} = 3\frac{5}{6}$
($\frac{1}{6}$)

b. $3\frac{5}{12}$
$+5\frac{7}{12}$
$8\frac{12}{12}$ = (9)

10.) a. $\frac{1}{100} = .01 = (1\%)$
b. $.001 = \frac{1}{1000} = (.1\%)$

11.) a. $\frac{13}{52}$ b. $\frac{1}{52}$ c. $\frac{26}{52}$

12.) $\frac{.6912789\ mi}{sec.} \times \frac{60\ sec.}{1\ min.} \times \frac{60\ min.}{1\ hr.}$
(= 2,488.604 miles)

1.) a. $4\frac{1}{2} \times 4\frac{1}{4} = \frac{9}{2} \times \frac{17}{4} = \frac{153}{8} = (19\frac{1}{8})$
b. $\frac{15}{16} \div 1\frac{7}{8} = \frac{15}{16} \div \frac{15}{8} = \frac{15}{16} \times \frac{8}{15} = (\frac{1}{2})$

2.) a. 15 ÷ .03
1500 ÷ 3 = (500)
b. .15 ÷ .03 =
15 ÷ 3 = (5)

3.) (b)

4.) 313,000,000 (3.13×10^8)

5.) a. ($0 < a \le 3$)
b.

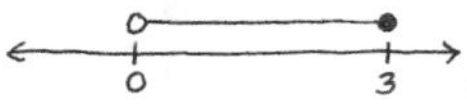

6.) increase by 50% =
100% + 50% = 150% = 1.5
a. 1.5x = 90 $x = \frac{90}{1.5}$ 90 ÷ 1.5 = ($60)
b. 3% x 90 = ($2.70)

7.) a. 4,000 x 300 =
(1,200,000)
b. 72,000,000 ÷ 9,000 =
(8,000)

8.) (12)

9.) a. $\frac{3}{7}x = \frac{15}{22}$
$\frac{7}{3} \cdot \frac{3}{7}x = \frac{15}{22} \cdot \frac{7}{3}$
$x = \frac{35}{22} = (1\frac{13}{22})$

b. $\frac{5}{9}x = 60$
$\frac{9}{5} \cdot \frac{5}{9}x = 60 \cdot \frac{9}{5}$
($x = 108$)

c. $-\frac{3}{11}x = \frac{3}{44}$
$-\frac{11}{3} \cdot -\frac{3}{11}x = \frac{3}{44} \cdot -\frac{11}{3}$
$x = (-\frac{1}{4})$

10.) Alternate counting back from 100 by 5's with counting forward from 2 by 2's. (80, 10, 75, 12)

11.) $4\frac{1}{2} \div \frac{3}{8} =$
$\frac{9}{2} \div \frac{3}{8} =$
$\frac{9}{2} \times \frac{8}{3} =$
(12 bows)

b. (no left overs)

12.) a. A = 12 x 14 = (168 ft.²)
b. $\frac{168}{9} = 18.\bar{6}$
(19 sq. yards)

1.) a. $3\frac{1}{2} + 2\frac{1}{8} =$
$\frac{7}{2} + \frac{17}{8} =$
$\frac{28}{8} + \frac{17}{8} = \frac{45}{8} = 5\frac{5}{8}$

b. $6\frac{1}{8} - 2\frac{3}{4} =$
$\frac{49}{8} - \frac{11}{4} =$
$\frac{49}{8} - \frac{22}{8} = \frac{27}{8} = 3\frac{3}{8}$

2.) $2 \times 29 \times 50 = 2 \times 50 \times 29 =$ 2900

3.) $\frac{101+128+98+156+130}{5} =$ 122.6 or 123

4.) a. $30{,}157 \div 29 \approx 30{,}000 \div 30 = 1{,}000$
b. $4{,}189 \times 512 \approx 4{,}000 \times 500 = 2{,}000{,}000$

5.) a. $8 = 7\frac{10}{10}$; $-2\frac{3}{10} = -2\frac{3}{10}$; $5\frac{7}{10}$
b. $2\frac{3}{4} = 2\frac{3}{4}$; $+1\frac{1}{2} = 1\frac{2}{4}$; $3\frac{5}{4} = 4\frac{1}{4}$

6.) a. $a + 2a = 90°$
b. $3a = 90°$
$a = 30°$ $2a = 60°$

7.) factors: 63 = 1, 3, 7, (9), 21, 63
54 = 1, 2, 3, 6, (9), 18, 27, 54
81 = 1, 3, (9), 27, 81, GCF = 9

8.) a. 31,100
b. 999

9.) a. $\frac{19}{16} \times \frac{11}{10} = \frac{209}{60} = 3\frac{29}{60}$
b. $\frac{1}{2} \div 1\frac{1}{4} = \frac{1}{2} \div \frac{5}{4}$; $\frac{1}{2} \times \frac{4}{5} = \frac{2}{5}$

10.) a. 18.5% = .185
b. 200% = 2.00
c. .5% = .005

11.) 11:25
9:45
10:58
30:128 = 32 hrs. 8 min.

12.) a. $\frac{1}{6}$
b. $\frac{3}{6}$
c. $\frac{1}{6}$

1.) a. $8x - 2 = -10$
$+2 \quad +2$
$8x = -8$
$\frac{1}{8} \cdot 8x = -8 \cdot \frac{1}{8}$
$x = -1$

b. $\frac{3}{4}x = 15$
$\frac{4}{3} \cdot \frac{3}{4}x = 15 \cdot \frac{4}{3}$
$x = 20$

c. $1.2x = 3.6$
$x = 3$

2.) $7\frac{3}{8} = 7\frac{6}{16}$
$+13\frac{3}{16} = +13\frac{3}{16}$
$20\frac{9}{16}$

3.) a. $A = 10 \times 12 = 120\text{ ft}^2$
b. $18 \times 18 = 324\text{ in}^2$ $324\text{ in}^2 \times \frac{1\text{ ft}^2}{144\text{ in}^2} = 2.25\text{ ft}^2$
$\frac{120}{2.25} = 53.\bar{3}$ or 54 tiles

4.) $1\frac{1}{2} = 1.5$ $\frac{4.5}{1.5} = \$3$ per pound

5.) a. 9.709 + .001 = 9.710
b. 9.709 + .0001 = 9.7091

6.) 1,27562 1.27562×10^4

7.) about $5+1+1+7+4 \approx 18$ yes

8.) a. $x^2 = 16$ $x = \pm 4$
b. $|x| = 4$ $x = \pm 4$
c. $\sqrt{x} = 2$ $x = 4$

9.) a. $6 \times 3 \div 2$ (>) $6 \div 3 \times 2$
$18 \div 2$ 2×2
9 4

b. $(\frac{1}{2})^3$ (>) $(\frac{1}{3})^2$
$\frac{1}{8}$ $\frac{1}{9}$

c. 1.0^4 (=) $1000°$
1 1

d. $(-2)^3$ (<) 2^3
−8 8

10.) a. −7 and −6
b. −7

11.) C

12.) 42 is between 1-50; is divisible by 7; is an even number; ten's place (4) is twice one's place (2)

① a. $(2-4)^2/1+1$
$(-2)^2/1+1$
$4/1+1$
$4+1 = 5$

② $8-8/2 \times 2$
$8 - 4 \times 2$
$8 - 8 = 0$

③ $\frac{7-1^2}{4-2}$
$\frac{7-1}{2}$
$\frac{6}{2} = 3$

② a. $-2 \cdot -\frac{1}{2} = 1$
b. $(-2)^2 = 4$
c. $-(-\frac{1}{2})^2 = -(\frac{1}{4}) = -\frac{1}{4}$
d. $\frac{-\frac{1}{2}}{2}$
$-\frac{1}{2} \div 2$
$-\frac{1}{2} \cdot \frac{1}{2} = -\frac{1}{4}$
e. $-(-2)+2$
$2+2 = 4$
f. $-2 \cdot -\frac{1}{2} \cdot \frac{1}{2} \cdot 2 = 1$

③ a. $2n+5$ b. $\frac{1}{2}n - 6$ c. n^2+2 d. $-n$

④ a. $2a+3b-6a+b$
$2a-6a+3b+b$
$-4a+4b$

b. $4x^2 - x - 3x^2 + x$
$4x^2 - 3x^2 - x + x$
x^2

⑤ a. $\frac{2+2+3+0+2+9+8+8+4+2+3+25+80}{13} \approx 11.4$

b. 0 2 2 2 2 3 [3] 4 8 8 9 25 80

c. 2

d. Answers will vary. The median, 3, appears to be nearest to middle. When you look at the extreme values of 25 and 80, then the mean, 11.4, is closest to middle.

⑥ a. $\frac{12}{7}$ b. $\frac{12}{19}$

⑦ a. $3x+5 = -4$
$+-5 \quad +-5$
$3x = -9$
$\frac{1}{3} \cdot 3x = -9 \cdot \frac{1}{3}$
$x = -3$

b. $\frac{2}{3}x = 6$
$\frac{3}{2} \cdot \frac{2}{3}x = 6 \cdot \frac{3}{2}$
$x = 9$

c. $-x+8 = -4$
$+-8 \quad +-8$
$-x = -12$
$x = 12$

⑧ a. $4(x-y) = 4x - 4y$ b. $8a - 16 = 8(a - 2b)$

⑨ a. $x+y = 3$
$0+3 = 3$ (0,3)
$1+2 = 3$ (1,2)
$3+0 = 3$ (3,0)

b.

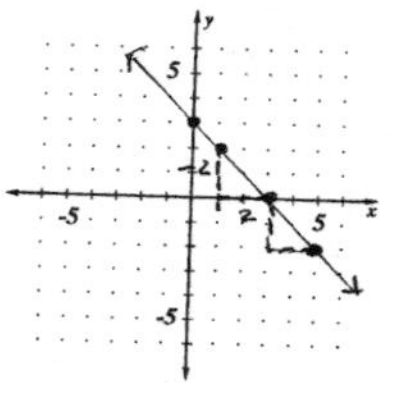

c. rise = −2 run = 2
$\frac{\text{rise}}{\text{run}} = \frac{-2}{2} = -1$
(−2,5)

d. $-2+5 = 3$

⑩ a. 43200 = 4.32×10^4
b. 1000000 = 1.0×10^6
c. .00502 = 5.02×10^{-3}
d. 5 = 5×10^0

① a. $4 \times 6 \div 3 \; \underline{=} \; 6 \div 3 \times 4$
$24 \div 3 \quad 2 \times 4$
$8 = 8$

b. $\left(\frac{1}{2}\right)^3 \; \underline{>} \; \left(\frac{1}{3}\right)^2$
$\frac{1}{8} > \frac{1}{9}$

c. $\frac{1}{4} \times \frac{1}{4} \; \underline{<} \; \frac{1}{4} \div \frac{1}{4}$
$\frac{1}{16} \quad \frac{1}{4} \cdot \frac{4}{1}$
$\frac{1}{16} < 1$

d. $1.0^6 \; \underline{=} \; 1000000^0$
$1 = 1$

e. $4-(4\div 4)\times 4 \; \underline{=} \; (4-4)\div 4\times 4$
$4-1\times 4 \quad 0\div 4\times 4$
$4-4 \quad 0\times 4$
$0 = 0$

f. $2\times 3+4 \; \underline{<} \; 2+3\times 4$
$6+4 \quad 2+12$
$10 < 14$

② a. $4=\frac{4}{1}$ b. $-8=\frac{-8}{1}$ c. $.9=\frac{9}{10}$ d. $.125=\frac{125}{1000}$
e. $25\% = .25 = \frac{25}{100}$ f. $.\overline{3}=\frac{3}{9}$ g. $.3=\frac{3}{10}$ h. $6.5\% = .065 = \frac{65}{1000}$

③ a. $rt=d$ b. $.10n=5.50$ c. $7>2a$ d. $10<3n$

④ a. 8 b. 4 c. $4+8=12$

⑤ a. $3a-b-3a$
$3a-3a-b=$ ($-b$)

b. $2(x+y)-2x+2y$
$2x+2y-2x+2y$
$2x-2x+2y+2y=$
($4y$)

c. $2(4x)^2$
$2\cdot 16x^2$
($32x^2$)

⑥ a. 14, 18 b. $6-2=4$
c. examples: next term is previous term +4
or (1) Find the zero term: $2-4=-2$
(2) $t=4n-2$
d. $t=4(10)-2=38$

⑦ a. $\frac{2}{3}=\frac{21}{33}$ no
$63 \neq 66$
b. $\frac{5}{6}=\frac{83}{100}$ no
$498 \neq 500$
c. $\frac{4}{5}=\frac{16}{20}$ yes
$80=80$

⑧ a. $C=2\pi r$
$C=2\pi\cdot 2$
$=4\pi$ inches
b. $4(3.14)\approx 12.56 \approx 12.6$ inches

⑨ a. commutative property
b. distributive property
c. associative property

⑩ a. $(-2)^2-(-2)$
$4+2=$ (6)
b. $(-2)^3+(-2)^2+(-2)$
$-8+4-2=$ (-6)
c. $|-2|=$ (2)

① a. $(6+2)^2/16\times 4$
$8^2/16\times 4$
$64/16\times 4$
$4\times 4=$ (16)

b. $8-2^3/2$
$8-8/2$
$8-4=$ (4)

c. $\frac{8-2^3}{2}$
$\frac{8-8}{2}$
$\frac{0}{2}=$ (0)

② $m=\frac{y_2-y_1}{x_2-x_1} \quad \frac{-8-4}{2-0} = \frac{-12}{2} = -6$

③ a. $25\% = .25 = \frac{25}{100}$ R b. $\sqrt{2}\approx 1.414$ I

c. $\sqrt{\frac{1}{4}}=\frac{1}{2}$ R d. $\pi \approx 3.14$ I e. $\frac{22}{7}$ R

④ a. $\frac{81+85+87+92+98}{5} = 88.6$

b. $\frac{81+85+87+92+98+x}{6} = 90$
$443+x=540$
$x=97$

⑤ e. trapezoid $A=\frac{1}{2}h(b_1+b_2)$
f. square $A=s^2$
a. rectangle $A=lw$
b. circle $A=\pi r^2$
d. triangle $A=\frac{1}{2}hb$
c. parallelogram $A=bh$

⑥ a. $x+3x=180$
b. $x+3x=180$
$4x=180$
$x=45°$ $3x=135°$

⑦ Let $a=4$ Let $b=\frac{1}{4}$ Let $c=-4$ Let $d=-\frac{1}{4}$

a. $4^{-1} \; \underline{<} \; \left(\frac{1}{4}\right)^{-1}$
$\frac{1}{4} < 4$

b. $\left(\frac{1}{4}\right)^2 \; \underline{=} \; \left(-\frac{1}{4}\right)^2$
$\frac{1}{16} = \frac{1}{16}$

c. $4^0 \; \underline{=} \; -4^0$
$1 = 1$

d. $\frac{1}{4} \; \underline{>} \; \left(\frac{1}{4}\right)^2$
$\frac{1}{4} > \frac{1}{16}$

e. $-(4)^2 \; \underline{<} \; (-4)^2$
$-16 < 16$

f. $4+(-4) \; \underline{=} \; \frac{1}{4}+\left(-\frac{1}{4}\right)$
$0=0$

⑧ 15 marbles
a. $P(\text{green})=\frac{5}{15}=\frac{1}{3}$
b. "or" means add
$P(\text{blue or red})=\frac{8}{15}+\frac{2}{15}=\frac{10}{15}=\frac{2}{3}$
c. $P(\text{not blue})=1-\frac{8}{15}=\frac{7}{15}$
d. $P(\text{black})=\frac{0}{15}=0$ impossible
e. "and" means multiply
$P(\text{first red and second green})=\frac{2}{15}\cdot\frac{5}{14}=\frac{1}{21}$

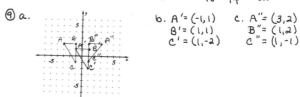

⑨ a.

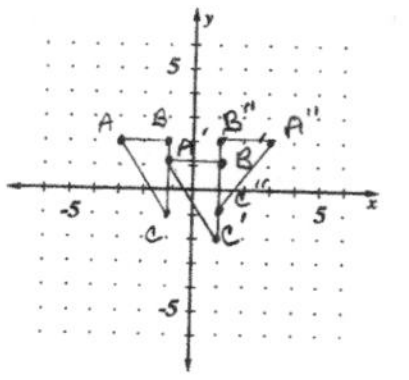

b. $A'=(-1,1)$
$B'=(1,1)$
$C'=(1,-2)$

c. $A''=(3,2)$
$B''=(1,2)$
$C''=(1,-1)$

① a. $x^2 = 25$
$x = +5$ or -5
or ± 5

b. $|x| = 2$
$x = +2$ or -2
or ± 2

c. $2^x = 16$
$2^x = 2^4$
$x = 4$

② a.

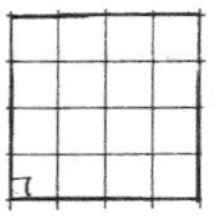

b.

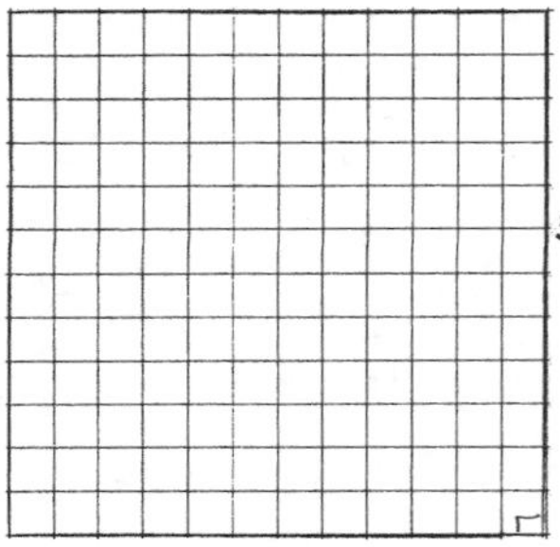

c. $P_{sm} = 4(1) = 4$ in
$P_{lg} = 4(3) = 12$in

d. $A_{sm} = 1^2 = 1$ sq. in.
$A_{lg} = 3^2 = 9$ sq. in.

e. 3 f. 9

③ a. $m\angle 1 = 135°$ b. $m\angle 2 = 135°$
c. $m\angle 3 = 45°$ d. $m\angle 4 = 65°$

④ a. $A = \frac{1}{2}h(b_1 + b_2)$ $A = \frac{1}{2}(4)(6+8) = 2(14) = 28$ in^2

b. $32 = \frac{1}{2}(4)(2b)$ $32 = 4b$ $b_1 = 8$in $b_2 = 8$in

⑤ $c^2 = a^2 + b^2$
$c^2 = 5^2 + 12^2$
$c^2 = 169$
$c = 13$ units

⑥ a. 14 b. 0 c. 7
d. 10 e. 5 f. $10 - 5 = 5$

⑦ Products:
$20 \cdot -1 = -20$ $-20 \cdot 1 = -21$ $-10 + 2 = -8$ -10 and 2
$10 \cdot -2 = -20$ $-10 \cdot 2 = -20$

⑧ $A = \pi r^2$
$85 = \pi r^2$
$r^2 \approx 27.05$
$r \approx 5.2$ ft.
$d = 2r = 10.4$ ft.

⑨ a. $\frac{x}{6} = \frac{3}{8}$
$18 = 8x$
$x = 2.25$

b. $\frac{x}{15} = \frac{5}{75}$
$75 = 75x$
$x = 1$

c. $\frac{x^2}{4} = \frac{9}{25}$
$25x^2 = 36$
$x^2 = \frac{36}{25}$
$x = \pm \frac{6}{5}$

① a. $p = 4s$
$1 = 4s$ $s = \frac{1}{4}$ mile

b. $A = s^2$
$A = (\frac{1}{4})^2 = \frac{1}{16}$ miles^2

② a. 4 b. -3 c. 5th. d. 1

③ The audience was probably mostly adults. Adults might not be as happy about gum chewing in class as students might be.

④ a. $P(4 \text{ boys}) = \frac{1}{16}$

b. $P(2 \text{ boys } \& \text{ } 2 \text{ girls}) = \frac{6}{16}$

c. $P(3 \text{ boys } \& \text{ } 1 \text{ girl}) = \frac{4}{16}$

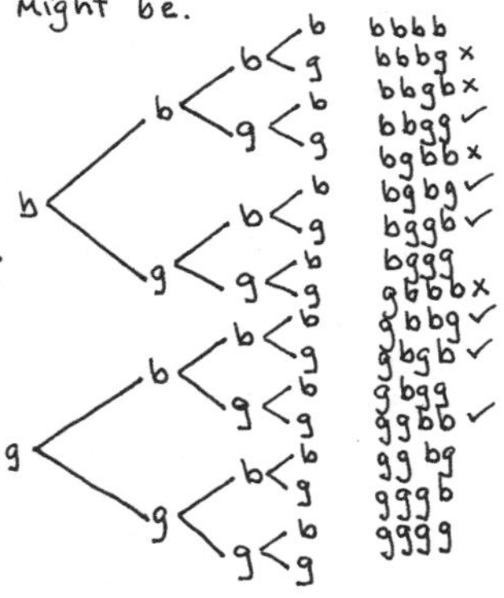

⑤ $c^2 = a^2 + b^2$ $(\sqrt{5})^2 = 1^2 + 2^2$ $5 = 1 + 4$ ✓

⑥ a. group $2.30 + 1.70$
\$8.95

b. group $-5 + 5$
10

c. group $3 \cdot \frac{1}{3}$
17

d. group $\frac{1}{3} + \frac{2}{3}$ $\frac{1}{5} + \frac{4}{5}$

⑦ a. $\frac{1}{3}(3) = 1$ b. $(\frac{2}{5})(\frac{5}{2}) = 1$ c. $.1(10) = 1$
d. $\frac{1}{n} \cdot n = 1$

⑧ a. $x - y = 4$
$4 - 0 = 4$ $(4,0)$
$5 - 1 = 4$ $(5,1)$
$0 - (-4) = 4$ $(0,-4)$

b.

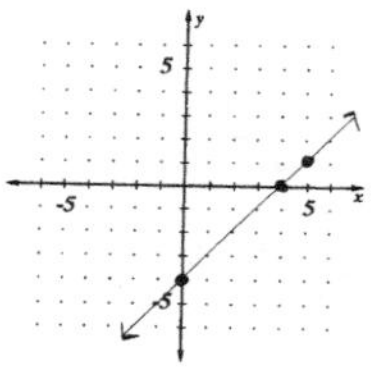

c. $m = \frac{y_2 - y_1}{x_2 - x_1} = \frac{1-0}{5-4} = 1$

⑨ a. $T_{-2,-1}(2,1) = (0,0)$ b. $r_{x\text{-axis}}(2,1) = (2,-1)$
c. $r_{y\text{-axis}}(2,1) = (-2,1)$

⑩ a. $x = -3$ -2 -1 0 1 2 3
$y = 9$ 4 1 0 1 4 9

b.

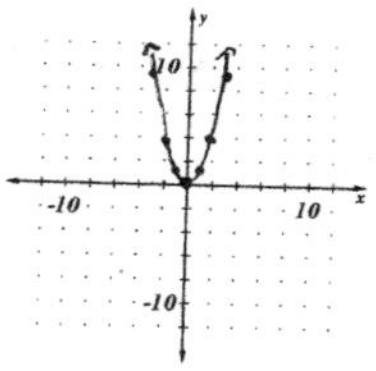

c. parabola

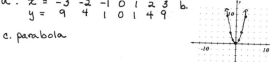

⑪ $4! = 4 \cdot 3 \cdot 2 \cdot 1 = 24$

⑫ a. $3n + -n = -8$
b. $3n + -n = -8$
$2n = -8$
$n = -4$

Summer Math Skills Lesson Tracker

Book Grade Level ______________ **Name of Student** ___________________________________

Lesson #	# of Problems	# of Problems Completed	# of Problems Incorrect	Parent/Tutor Initials
1				
2				
3				
4				
5				
6				
7				
8				
9				
10				
11				
12				
13				
14				
15				
16				
17				
18				
19				
20				
21				
22				
23				

Lesson #	# of Problems	# of Problems Completed	# of Problems Incorrect	Parent/Tutor Initials
24				
25				
26				
27				
28				
29				
30				
31				
32				
33				
34				
35				

Extras (Brain Aerobics, Math Facts Sharpener)

Questions	# Completed	# Correct	# Incorrect	Parent/Tutor Initials

Parent/Tutor Signature ______________________________

Manuscript

WHITE PAPER

Format			Size	ISBN
4 stave	24pp	*wide ruling with ledger guides*	A5 148 x 210mm	0-571-52700-0
6 stave	64pp	*spiral bound*	A5 148 x 210mm	0-571-52701-9
8 stave	64pp	*guitar tab with chord boxes, tear-off pad*	A4 297 x 210mm	0-571-52702-7
10 stave	64pp	*spiral bound*	A4 297 x 210mm	0-571-52703-5
10 stave	100pp	*tear-off pad*	A4 297 x 210mm	0-571-52704-3
12 stave	32pp	*wired book*	A4 297 x 210mm	0-571-52705-1
12 stave	64pp	*spiral bound*	A4 297 x 210mm	0-571-52706-X
12 stave	100pp	*tear-off pad*	A4 297 x 210mm	0-571-52707-8
12 stave	200pp	*tear-off pad*	A4 297 x 210mm	0-571-52708-6
18 stave	75pp	*tear-off pad*	A3 297 x 420mm	0-571-52709-4

CREAM PAPER

Format			Size	ISBN
6 stave	24pp	*wired book*	A5 148 x 210mm	0-571-52710-8
6 stave	24pp	*interleaved*	A5 148 x 210mm	0-571-52711-6
12 stave	32pp	*wired book*	A4 297 x 210mm	0-571-52712-4
12 stave	64pp	*spiral bound*	A4 297 x 210mm	0-571-52713-2

FABER MUSIC

FABER MUSIC · 3 QUEEN SQUARE · LONDON
fabermusic.com

ISBN10: 0-571-5270
EAN13: 978-0-571-52706-9

9780571527069

DIATONIC CHORDS & INVERSIONS:

The most common type of chord is the TRIAD, which may be described as the simultaneous sounding either of 'three alternate SCALE-DEGREES' or of 'two superimposed THIRDS'. Those of C MAJOR are as follows:

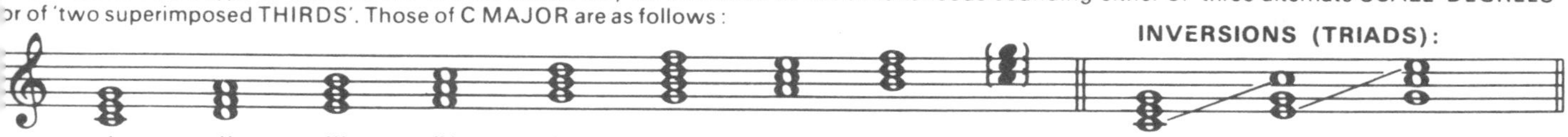

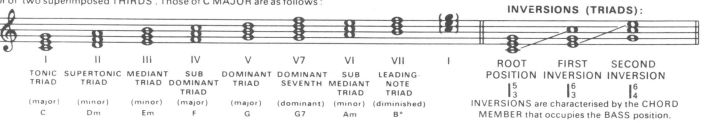

I	II	III	IV	V	V7	VI	VII	I
TONIC TRIAD	SUPERTONIC TRIAD	MEDIANT TRIAD	SUB DOMINANT TRIAD	DOMINANT TRIAD	DOMINANT SEVENTH	SUB MEDIANT TRIAD	LEADING-NOTE TRIAD	
(major)	(minor)	(minor)	(major)	(major)	(dominant)	(minor)	(diminished)	
C	Dm	Em	F	G	G7	Am	B°	

ROOT POSITION	FIRST INVERSION	SECOND INVERSION
5 3	6 3	6 4

INVERSIONS are characterised by the CHORD MEMBER that occupies the BASS position.

CLASSIFICATION OF INTERVALS & DISSONANCE:

Any two pitches—consecutive or simultaneous—constitute an INTERVAL which can be indentified by either of two methods TONAL CONTEXT—in which the interval is measured by SCALE-DEGREE from the ROOT, and PITCH CLASS SET—whereby the interval is measured in SEMITONES counting from the lower note. The second method is used to describe NON-TONAL music wherein TONAL nomenclature would be misleading.

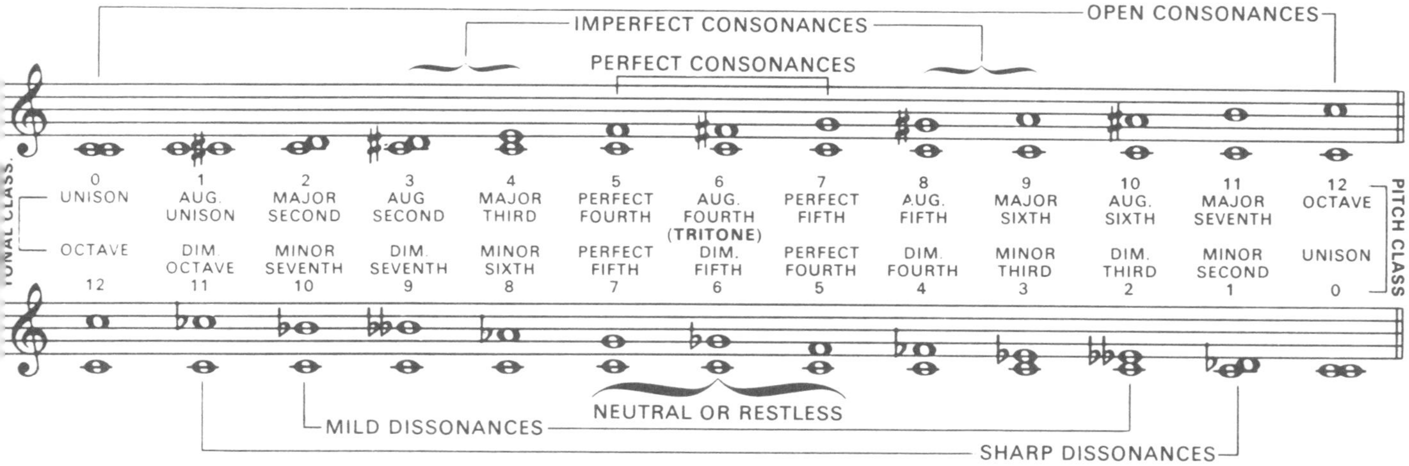

Pitch class	0	1	2	3	4	5	6	7	8	9	10	11	12
Tonal class	UNISON	AUG. UNISON	MAJOR SECOND	AUG SECOND	MAJOR THIRD	PERFECT FOURTH	AUG. FOURTH (TRITONE)	PERFECT FIFTH	AUG. FIFTH	MAJOR SIXTH	AUG. SIXTH	MAJOR SEVENTH	OCTAVE
Tonal class	OCTAVE	DIM. OCTAVE	MINOR SEVENTH	DIM. SEVENTH	MINOR SIXTH	PERFECT FIFTH	DIM. FIFTH	PERFECT FOURTH	DIM. FOURTH	MINOR THIRD	DIM. THIRD	MINOR SECOND	UNISON
Pitch class	12	11	10	9	8	7	6	5	4	3	2	1	0

INTERVALS larger than an OCTAVE are called COMPOUND INTERVALS and, since they are, in reality, OCTAVE DISPLACEMENTS of one or other elements of a SIMPLE INTERVAL (i.e. an OCTAVE or less) they are not given here.

TIME SIGNATURES & METRE:

A TIME SIGNATURE is a vertical arrangement of two numerals on the STAVE, placed immediately after the CLEF and the KEY SIGNATURE. In SIMPLE TIME, the upper numeral indicates the NUMBER OF BEATS within each BAR (or MEASURE) whilst the lower numeral gives the NOTE VALUE (or RELATIVE DURATION) that these BEATS have. In COMPOUND TIME the upper numeral indicates the number of INNER PULSATIONS within each BAR, whereas the lower numeral gives the NOTE VALUE of these INNER PULSATIONS.

DUPLE	Simple:	2/2	2/4	2/8
DUPLE	Compound:	6/4	6/8	6/16
QUADRUPLE	Simple:	4/2	4/4	4/8
QUADRUPLE	Compound:	12/4	12/8	12/16
TRIPLE	Simple:	3/2	3/4	3/8
TRIPLE	Compound:	9/4	9/8	9/16

The diagram illustrates METRES in PERFECT TIME—i.e. those in which the upper numeral of the TIME SIGNATURE is divisible by two or three (those which are not so divisible belong to IMPERFECT TIME and include QUINTUPLE and SEPTUPLE METRES).